To Beverly for your 16th ... from Mrs. Moor.

Gems

of

Grace

and

Glory

▼

Compiled by

EDWARD BOONE

D. E. PRICE

C. E. MYERS

N. B. VANDAL

▼

PRICES

	Manila Binding	Cloth
Single copy, postpaid	$ .25	$ .40
25 copies, not postpaid	4.00	7.00
50 copies, not postpaid	7.50	13.50
100 copies, not postpaid	15.00	27.00

The BOONE PUBLISHING CO.

no place to lay His head

Box 200, Des Moines, Iowa

Gems
of
Grace
and
Glory

We have selected, with the greatest care, the songs for this book which we believe will be mostly used by the average congregation. We have some very choice numbers, recently composed, that we are offering for the first time in this book. Included are some splendid children's songs and choruses.

We are grateful and deeply indebted to D. E. Price, of Detroit, Michigan, C. E. Myers of Osborn, Missouri, and N. B. Vandal of Cleveland, Ohio, for their assistance and co-operation in compiling this book.

It is with a prayer we send it forth, trusting "Gems of Grace and Glory" will be a great blessing to the cause of Jesus Christ, and that many who know Him not as their personal Savior, will be made to realize their need of Christ through the medium of the songs.

RADIO PERMISSION

All songs owned and copyrighted by The Boone Publishing Company, printed in any of our publications, are free to use at any time over any radio station.

Sincerely yours,

THE BOONE PUBLISHING COMPANY

1   Grace and Glory

Edward Boone   COPYRIGHT, 1941, BY THE BOONE PUBLISHING CO.   Edward Boone

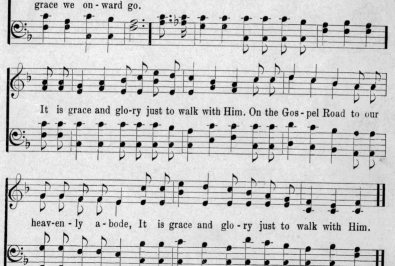

1. Oh, the Lord, our God, is a sun and shield Un-to those who trust in Him; If they walk up-right-ly and each day shine bright-ly, And they help some soul to win.

2. As the sun-light shines on this world be-low So the Lord sends forth His ray; With His pres-ence near us how His love does cheer us, And it helps us on our way.

3. He's a might-y shield from the darts of sin As you trav-el to and fro; He's a sure pro-tec-tion, and from each di-rec-tion He will shield you from the foe.

4. His sus-tain-ing grace, He so free-ly gives On the Sun-shine Route be-low; Here our hearts are sing-ing and the joy-bells ring-ing As with grace we on-ward go.

CHORUS

It is grace and glo-ry since He saves from sin; It is grace and glo-ry just to walk with Him. On the Gos-pel Road to our heav-en-ly a-bode, It is grace and glo-ry just to walk with Him.

No. 2. At the Cross.

I. WATTS. R. E. HUDSON.

1. A - las! and did my Sav - ior bleed, And did my Sovereign die,
2. Was it for crimes that I have done, He groaned upon the tree?
3. But drops of grief can ne'er re - pay, The debt of love I owe;

Would He de-vote that sa - cred head For such a worm as I?
A - maz - ing pit - y, grace unknown, And love be-yond de-gree!
Here, Lord I give my - self a-way, 'Tis all that I can do!

CHORUS.

At the cross, at the cross, where I first saw the light, And the

bur-den of my heart rolled a - way— It was there by faith
rolled a - way,

I re-ceived my sight, And now I am hap-py all the day.

24

3 Sweeter Than All.

Johnson Oatman, Jr.

COPYRIGHT, 1900, BY J. H. ENTWISLE.
J. J. HOOD, OWNER.

J. Howard Entwisle.

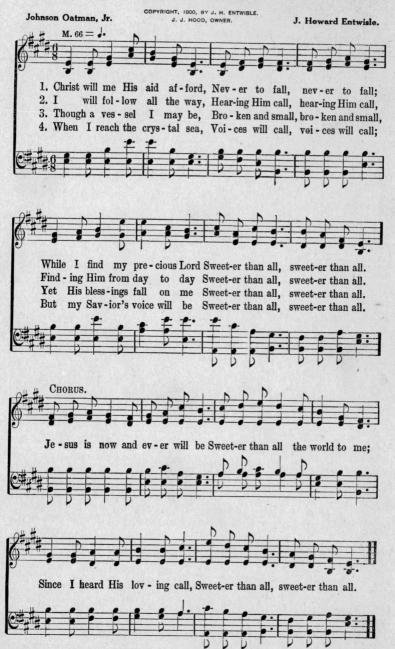

1. Christ will me His aid af-ford, Nev-er to fall, nev-er to fall;
2. I will fol-low all the way, Hear-ing Him call, hear-ing Him call,
3. Though a ves-sel I may be, Bro-ken and small, bro-ken and small,
4. When I reach the crys-tal sea, Voi-ces will call, voi-ces will call;

While I find my pre-cious Lord Sweet-er than all, sweet-er than all.
Find-ing Him from day to day Sweet-er than all, sweet-er than all.
Yet His bless-ings fall on me Sweet-er than all, sweet-er than all.
But my Sav-ior's voice will be Sweet-er than all, sweet-er than all.

CHORUS.

Je-sus is now and ev-er will be Sweet-er than all the world to me;

Since I heard His lov-ing call, Sweet-er than all, sweet-er than all.

Sweet By-and-By.

S. FILLMORE BENNETT.   JOS. P. WEBSTER.

1. There's a land that is fair-er than day, And by faith we can
2. We shall sing on that beau-ti-ful shore, The me-lo-di-ous
3. To our boun-ti-ful Fa-ther a-bove, We will of-fer our

see it a-far; For the Fa-ther waits o-ver the way, To pre-
songs of the blest, And our spir-its shall sor-row no more, Not a
trib-ute of praise, For the glo-ri-ous gift of his love, And the

CHORUS.

pare us a dwell-ing place there.
sigh for the bless-ing of rest.   In the sweet   by-and-
bless-ings that hal-low our days.   In the sweet

by,   We shall meet on that beau-ti-ful shore,   In the
   by-and-by,   by-and-by;

sweet   by-and-by,   We shall meet on that beau-ti-ful shore.
   by-and-by,   by-and-by,   by-and-by.

5 All the Way My Savior Leads.

Fanny J. Crosby. Robert Lowry.

1. All the way my Sav-ior leads me; What have I to ask be - side?
2. All the way my Sav-ior leads me, Cheers each wind-ing path I tread;
3. All the way my Sav-ior leads me; O the ful - ness of His love!

Can I doubt His ten-der mer - cy Who thro' life has been my guide?
Gives me grace for ev - 'ry tri - al, Feeds me with the liv - ing bread;
Per - fect rest to me is prom-ised In my Fa-ther's house a - bove;

Heav'n-ly peace, di - vin-est com-fort, Here by faith in Him to dwell!
Tho' my wea - ry steps may fal - ter, And my soul a - thirst may be,
When my spir - it, clothed, im-mor - tal, Wings its flight to realms of day,

For I know, what-e'er be - fall me, Je - sus do - eth all things well;
Gush - ing from the Rock be - fore me, Lo! a spring of joy I see;
This my song thro' end-less a - ges— Je - sus led me all the way;

For I know, what-e'er be - fall me, Je-sus do - eth all things well.
Gush-ing from the Rock be - fore me, Lo! a spring of joy I see.
This my song thro' end-less a - ges— Je - sus led me all the way.

The Pilot of Galilee

MRS. C. H. M.   MRS. C. H. MORRIS.

DUET. *Soprano and Alto.*

1. Out on life's o-cean with per-ils ev-er nigh, I have a
2. Wondrous His pow-er and matchless is His skill, Bil-lows and
3. Fierce was the tem-pest once rag-ing in my soul, When of my
4. Hear it ye storm-tossed up-on the sea of sin, Why will ye

Pi-lot on whom I can re-ly, With Him to guide me life's storms I can de-
tempests o-bey His sov'reign will, Hushed in-to si-lence at His blest "peace be
bark He my Pi-lot took con-trol, With voice commanding a-bove the thunder's
not take the heav'nly Pi-lot in? Safe-ly He'll guide you the ha-ven blest to

CHORUS.

fy, 'Tis Christ of Gal-i-lee.
still," This Man of Gal-i-lee.   He is my Pi-lot on life's stormy sea,
roll, This Man of Gal-i-lee.
win, This Man of Gal-i-lee.

This wondrous Man of Gal-i-lee; I'm safe in His keep-ing, tho'

storms are round me sweep-ing, This Pi-lot of Gal-i-lee.

Copyright, 1912, by H. L. Gilmore.

7 The Burden Is Gone

Mrs. Justin Lindley

Edward Boone

1. Grief-la-den and wea-ry I came to the Lord; He heard and He
2. My heart-cry to Him bro't me bless-ing un-told, As I in His
3. I fol-low Him glad-ly, He leads me in love To pas-tures where

an-swered my prayer. How changed is my life since He lift-ed the load Of
love now con-fide. The clouds have passed by; there's no gloom in the sky, Since
sweet wa-ter flows; His mer-cy sur-rounds me, His good-ness I prove, And

CHORUS

dark-ness and sor-row and care.
Je - sus has come to a - bide. The bur-den is gone since He came;
rich - es of grace He be-stows.

He an-swered my prayer, bless His name; And now all my cares and my

sor-row He shares. He's now and for-ev-er the same.

8 Glory to God, Hallelujah!

FANNY J. CROSBY. WM. J. KIRKPATRICK.

1. We are nev-er, nev-er wea-ry of the grand old song; Glo-ry to God,
2. We are lost a-mid the rap-ture of re-deem-ing love; Glo-ry to God,
3. We are go-ing to a pal-ace that is built of gold; Glo-ry to God,
4. There we'll shout redeeming mercy in a glad, new song; Glo-ry to God,

hal-le-lu-jah! We can sing it loud as ev-er, with our faith more strong:
hal-le-lu-jah! We are ris-ing on its pinions to the hills a-bove:
hal-le-lu-jah! Where the King in all his splendor we shall soon be-hold:
hal-le-lu-jah! There we'll sing the praise of Jesus with the blood-wash'd throng;

FINE. CHORUS.

Glo-ry to God, hal-le-lu-jah! O, the children of the Lord have a

right to shout and sing, For the way is grow-ing bright, and our

D.S.

souls are on the wing; We are go-ing by and by to the pal-ace of a King!

I. WATTS.

R. LOWRY.

Spirited.

1. Come we that love the Lord, And let our joys be known, Join
2. Let those re - fuse to sing Who nev - er knew our God; But
3. The hill of Zi - on yields A thous-and sa - cred sweets, Be-
4. Then let our songs a - bound, And ev - 'ry tear be dry; We're

in a song with sweet accord, Join in a song with sweet accord,
chil-dren of the heav'nly King, But children of the heav'nly King,
fore we reach the heav'nly fields, Be-fore we reach the heav'nly fields,
march-ing thro' Immanuel's ground, We're marching thro' Immanuel's ground,

And thus sur - round the throne, And thus surround the throne.
May speak their joys a-broad, May speak their joys a - broad.
Or walk the gold - en streets, Or walk the gold - en streets.
To fair - er worlds on high, To fair - er worlds on high.

And thus sur-round the throne, And thus sur - round the throne.

CHORUS.

We're march - ing to Zi - on, Beau - ti-ful, beau - ti-ful Zi - on; We're
We're march-ing on to Zi - on,

marching upward to Zi - on, The beau-ti-ful cit - y of God.
Zi - on, Zi-on,

Sound the Battle Cry.

W. F. S.   Wm. F. Sherwin.

1. Sound the bat - tle cry! See the foe is nigh; Raise the stand-ard high
2. Strong to meet the foe, March-ing on we go, While our cause we know,
3. O! Thou God of all, Hear us when we call, Help us one and all

For the Lord; Gird your ar - mor on, Stand firm, ev - 'ry one;
Must pre - vail; Shield and ban - ner bright, Gleaming in the light;
By Thy grace, When the bat - tle's done, And the vic - t'ry's won,

CHORUS.

Rest your cause up - on His ho - ly word. Rouse, then, sol - diers,
Bat - tling for the right We ne'er can fail.
May we wear the crown Be - fore Thy face.

ral - ly round the ban - ner, Read-y, stead-y, pass the word a-long; Onward,

forward, shout aloud Ho-san-na! Christ is Cap-tain of the might-y throng.

No. 11. Leaning on the Everlasting Arms.

Rev. E. A. HOFFMAN.

A. J. SHOWALTER.

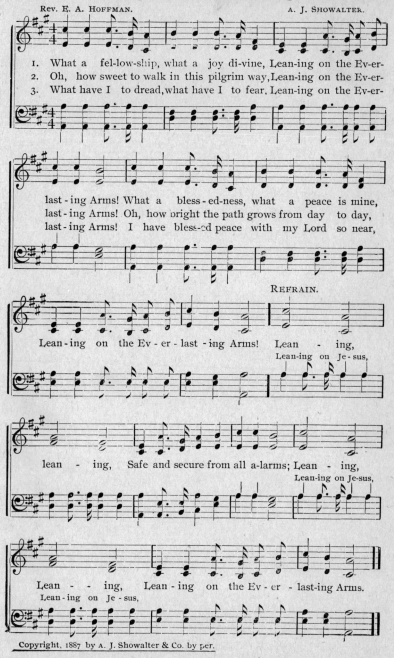

1. What a fel-low-ship, what a joy di-vine, Lean-ing on the Ev-er-
2. Oh, how sweet to walk in this pilgrim way, Lean-ing on the Ev-er-
3. What have I to dread, what have I to fear, Lean-ing on the Ev-er-

last-ing Arms! What a bless-ed-ness, what a peace is mine,
last-ing Arms! Oh, how bright the path grows from day to day,
last-ing Arms! I have bless-ed peace with my Lord so near,

REFRAIN.

Lean-ing on the Ev-er-last-ing Arms! Lean - - ing,
Lean-ing on Je-sus,

lean - - ing, Safe and secure from all a-larms; Lean - - ing,
Lean-ing on Je-sus,

Lean - - ing, Lean-ing on the Ev-er - last-ing Arms.
Lean-ing on Je-sus,

12 Saved By His Wonderful Grace.

Mrs. C. H. M. COPYRIGHT, 1922, BY THE CHRISTIAN WITNESS CO. Mrs. C. H. Morris.

1. God's won-der-ful grace is the theme of my song, His prais-es for-
2. As far as the East is re-moved from the West My sins He has
3. 'Twas down at the cross where sal-va-tion I found, And down at the

ev-er I'll sing;(I'll sing;)With full-est al-le-giance to Him I be-long, My
ta-ken a-way;(a-way;)With perfect sal-va-tion my soul He has blest, And
cross will I stay;(I'll stay;)Where pardon and cleansing for sin-ners a-bound, And

CHORUS.

bless-ed Re-deem-er and King. Saved! saved! saved! My sins are all under the
turned all my darkness to day.
where I'm kept saved ev'ry day.   My sins are all

blood;.... Saved! saved! saved! I'm shouting all glo-ry to God;....
un-der the blood;   to God;

Saved! saved! saved!.... And some day I'll look on His face;........
                      And some   day   I'll look on His face;

Saved By His Wonderful Grace

Saved! saved! saved!.... I'm saved by His won-der-ful grace.

won-der-ful grace.

No. 13   The King's Highway

Copyright, 1941, by The Boone Publishing Co.

Mrs. Justin Lindley

Edward Boone

1. Come, walk the King's highway, with me, A path se-cure, from danger free, With
2. The King's high-way, a glo-ry road, The distant tow'rs, the saint's abode. Soft
3. A love-ly place, this bor-der land, Where kindred souls walk hand in hand; While

light that gives a cheer-ing ray, While walk-ing in the King's high-way.
breez-es from the loft-y hills Bring ho-ly calm and na-ture stills.
they re-joice and prais-es sing, They walk the high-way with the King.

Chorus

Oh, let me walk in the King's highway, New pleasure to find from day to day,

The King in all His beau-ty see; Come, walk the King's highway with me.

Heavenly Sunlight.

"I am the Light of the world: he that followeth me shall not walk in the darkness."—John 8. 12.

Rev. H. J. ZELLEY.

G. H. COOK.

1. Walk-ing in sun-light, all of my jour-ney; O-ver the moun-tains thro' the deep vale; Je-sus has said I'll nev-er for-sake thee, Prom-ise di-vine that nev-er can fail.

2. Shad-ows a-round me, shad-ows a-bove me, Nev-er con-ceal my Sav-iour and Guide; He is the light, in Him is no dark-ness, Ev-er I'm walk-ing close to His side.

3. In the bright sun-light, ev-er re-joic-ing, Press-ing my way to man-sions a-bove; Sing-ing His prais-es glad-ly I'm walk-ing, Walk-ing in sun-light, sun-light of love.

CHORUS.

Heav-en-ly sun-light, heav-en-ly sun-light; Flooding my soul with glo-ry di-vine: Hal-le-lu-jah, I am re-joic-ing, Sing-ing His prais-es, Je-sus is mine.

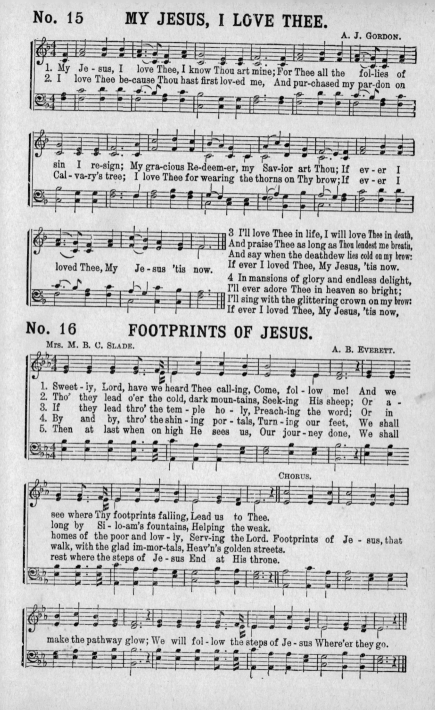

No. 15 MY JESUS, I LOVE THEE.

A. J. GORDON.

1. My Je-sus, I love Thee, I know Thou art mine; For Thee all the fol-lies of
2. I love Thee be-cause Thou hast first lov-ed me, And pur-chased my par-don on

sin I re-sign; My gra-cious Re-deem-er, my Sav-ior art Thou; If ev-er I
Cal-va-ry's tree; I love Thee for wearing the thorns on Thy brow; If ev-er I

loved Thee, My Je-sus 'tis now.

3 I'll love Thee in life, I will love Thee in death,
And praise Thee as long as Thou lendest me breath,
And say when the deathdew lies cold on my brow:
If ever I loved Thee, My Jesus, 'tis now.

4 In mansions of glory and endless delight,
I'll ever adore Thee in heaven so bright;
I'll sing with the glittering crown on my brow:
If ever I loved Thee, My Jesus, 'tis now,

No. 16 FOOTPRINTS OF JESUS.

Mrs. M. B. C. SLADE.   A. B. EVERETT.

1. Sweet-ly, Lord, have we heard Thee call-ing, Come, fol-low me! And we
2. Tho' they lead o'er the cold, dark moun-tains, Seek-ing His sheep; Or a-
3. If they lead thro' the tem-ple ho-ly, Preach-ing the word; Or in
4. By and by, thro' the shin-ing por-tals, Turn-ing our feet, We shall
5. Then at last when on high He sees us, Our jour-ney done, We shall

CHORUS.

see where Thy footprints falling, Lead us to Thee.
long by Si-lo-am's fountains, Helping the weak.
homes of the poor and low-ly, Serv-ing the Lord. Footprints of Je-sus, that
walk, with the glad im-mor-tals, Heav'n's golden streets.
rest where the steps of Je-sus End at His throne.

make the pathway glow; We will fol-low the steps of Je-sus Where'er they go.

17 He Lives Today

Mrs. Justin Lindley

Edward Boone

1. He lives to-day, our ris-en Lord; By faith we see the emp-ty tomb,
2. "He is not here," the an-gel said, For they have rolled a-way the stone;
3. He lives to-day—let heav-en ring With songs of ev-er-last-ing love,
4. He lives al-ways—let hearts re-joice; He'll come a-gain—oh, sweet re-lease;

And now He comes with ten-der word A-long the paths where lil-ies bloom.
And He who lay a-mong the dead—His her-it-age is now a throne.
While saints on earth may trib-ute bring And praise the One who reigns a-bove.
With trumpet sound His raptured voice Shall bring this world a last-ing peace.

CHORUS

Oh, ris-en Christ, ... He lives to-day; ..... Redeeming grace .....
Oh, ris-en Christ,   He lives to-day;   Redeeming grace

He free-ly gives; ..... He is the Light, ... the Truth, the Way; .....
He free-ly gives;   He is the Light,   the Truth, the Way;

Be-yond the tomb .... our Sav-iour lives ....
Be-yond the tomb   our Sav-iour lives.

18 Such Love.

C. Bishop.

Robert Harkness.

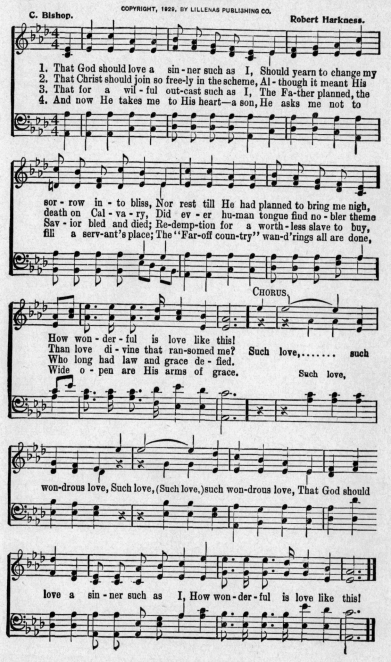

1. That God should love a sin-ner such as I, Should yearn to change my
2. That Christ should join so free-ly in the scheme, Al-though it meant His
3. That for a wil-ful out-cast such as I, The Fa-ther planned, the
4. And now He takes me to His heart—a son, He asks me not to

sor-row in-to bliss, Nor rest till He had planned to bring me nigh,
death on Cal-va-ry, Did ev-er hu-man tongue find no-bler theme
Sav-ior bled and died; Re-demp-tion for a worth-less slave to buy,
fill a serv-ant's place; The "Far-off coun-try" wan-d'rings all are done,

CHORUS.

How won-der-ful is love like this!
Than love di-vine that ran-somed me? Such love,....... such
Who long had law and grace de-fied.
Wide o-pen are His arms of grace. Such love,

won-drous love, Such love, (Such love,) such won-drous love, That God should

love a sin-ner such as I, How won-der-ful is love like this!

It Is Mine.

Elisha A. Hoffman.   Wm. Edie Marks.

1. God's a - bid - ing peace is in my soul to - day, Yes, I feel it
2. He has wrought in me a sweet and per - fect rest, In my rap - tured
3. He has giv - en me a nev - er fail - ing joy, O I have it
4. O the love of God is com - fort - ing my soul, For His love is

now, Yes, I feel it now; He has ta - ken all my doubts and fears a -
heart, I can feel it now; He each passing moment keeps me sav'd and
now, O I have it now; To His praise I will my ransom'd pow'rs em -
mine, yes, His love is mine; Waves of joy and glad-ness o'er my spir - it

CHORUS.

way, Tho' I can-not tell you how. It is mine,   mine,
blest, Floods with light my heart and brow.
ploy, And re-new my grateful vow.
roll, Thrilling me with love di-vine. It is mine, this priceless treasure, ev-er

blessed be His name! He has giv-en peace, perfect peace to me; It is

mine,   mine,   blessed be His name! Mine for all e- ter- ni- ty.
mine, this price-less treas-ure ev-er.

No. 20 There Shall Be Showers of Blessing.

El Nathan.　　　　　　　　　　　　　　　　James McGranahan.

M.63 = ♩

1. "There shall be show-ers of bless-ing"—This is the prom-ise of love;
2. "There shall be show-ers of bless-ing"—Precious, re - viv - ing a - gain,
3. "There shall be show-ers of bless-ing"—Send them up - on us, O Lord!
4. "There shall be show-ers of bless-ing"—O that to - day they might fall,

There shall be sea-sons re-fresh-ing, Sent from the Sav - ior a - bove.
O - ver the hills and the val - leys Sound of a - bun-dance of rain.
Grant to us now a re - fresh-ing, Come, and now hon - or Thy Word!
Now as to God we're con-fess-ing, Now as on Je - sus we call!

CHORUS.

Show - - - ers of bless - ing, Show-ers of bless-ing we need;
Show - ers, show-ers

Mer - cy-drops round us are fall - ing, But for the show-ers we plead.

21 Saved By the Blood.

B. M. L.   Bertha Mae Lillenas.

1. Saved by the blood of the Cru-ci-fied One, Washed and made whiter than snow;
2. Saved by the blood of the Cru-ci-fied One, I am a child of His love;
3. Saved by the blood of the Cru-ci-fied One, Heir to His rich-es of grace;
4. Saved by the blood of the Cru-ci-fied One, Soon I shall look on His face;

Life ev-er-last-ing with-in me be-gun, Saved by the blood of the Lamb!
Free-ly for-giv-en, my bur-den is gone! Saved by the blood of the Lamb!
Trust-ing in Him I find heaven be-gun, Saved by the blood of the Lamb!
Meet Him in glo-ry when life's race is run, Saved by the blood of the Lamb!

CHORUS.

Saved,   saved,

Saved by the blood, saved by the blood, Saved by the blood of the Crucified One;
Saved,   saved, saved,   saved,

Saved,   saved,

Saved by the blood, saved by the blood, Saved by the merit of God's on-ly Son,
Saved,   saved, saved,   saved,

Gone are my burdens and gone are my fears, Gone are the heartaches of many long years.

Saved by the Blood

Sim-ply be-liev-ing, I cast off my fears, Saved by the blood of the Lamb!
by the blood of the Lamb!

No. 22 **Praises**

Copyright, 1941, by The Boone Publishing Co.

Mrs. Justin Lindley   Edward Boone

1. At morn - ing I will praise Him For watch-care thru the night,
2. At noon - day I will praise Him For grace to meet each test,
3. At ev'n - ing I will praise Him Be - cause He led me thru
4. At mid - night I will praise Him, When darkness shrouds my way,

For heart of love to serve Him Tho' path be dim or bright.
And for the blest as - sur - ance, He giv - eth what is best.
Each tri - al and temp - ta - tion And gives me strength a - new.
And trust in Him to guide me Un - til the break of day.

Chorus

I'll praise Him, ev - er praise Him; His lov - ing voice I hear.

He gives me songs of glad - ness To si - lence ev - 'ry fear.

Saved to the Uttermost.

W. J. K.   Wm. J. Kirkpatrick.

1. Saved to the ut-ter-most: I am the Lord's; Je-sus my Sav-ior sal-
2. Saved to the ut-ter-most: Je-sus is near; Keeping me safe-ly, He
3. Saved to the ut-ter-most: this I can say, "Once all was dark-ness, but
4. Saved to the ut-ter-most: cheer-ful-ly sing Loud hal-le-lu-jahs to

va-tion af-fords; Gives me His Spir-it a wit-ness with-in,
cast-eth out fear; Trust-ing His prom-is-es, how I am blest;
now it is day; Beau-ti-ful vi-sions of glo-ry I see,
Je-sus my King! Ran-somed and par-doned, re-deemed by His blood,

REFRAIN.

Whisp'ring of par-don, and sav-ing from sin.
Lean-ing up-on Him, how sweet is my rest. Saved, saved,
Je-sus in bright-ness re-vealed un-to me.
Cleansed from un-right-eous-ness, glo-ry to God.

saved to the ut-ter-most: Saved, saved by pow-er di-vine; Saved, saved,

saved to the ut-ter-most: Je-sus the Sav-ior is mine.

He Rolled the Sea Away.

Rev. H. J. Zelley.   COPYRIGHT, 1896, BY H. L. GILMOUR.   H. L. Gilmour.

1. When Is - rael out of bond-age came, A sea be - fore them lay;
2. Be - fore me was a sea of sin, So great I feared to pray;
3. When sor-rows dark, like storm-y waves, Were dash - ing o'er my way;
4. And when I reach the sea of death, For need - ed grace I'll pray;

My Lord reach'd down His might-y hand, And roll'd the sea a - way.
My heart's de-sire the Sav - ior read, And roll'd the sea a - way.
A - gain the Lord in mer - cy came, And roll'd the sea a - way.
I know the Lord will quick - ly come, And roll the sea a - way.

CHORUS.

Then for-ward still, 'tis Je - ho-vah's will, Tho' the billows dash and spray;

With a conqu'ring tread we will push a-head, He'll roll the sea a - way.

No. 25 Shall We Gather at the River?

R. L.

Robert Lowry.

1. Shall we gath-er at the riv-er, Where bright angel feet have trod;
2. On the mar-gin of the riv-er, Wash-ing up its sil-ver spray;
3. Ere we reach the shining riv-er, Lay we ev-'ry bur-den down;
4. Soon we'll reach the silver riv-er, Soon our pil-grim-age will cease:

With its crys-tal tide for-ev-er Flow-ing by the throne of God?
We will walk and worship ev-er All the hap-py, gold-en day.
Grace our spir-its will de-liv-er And pro-vide a robe and crown.
Soon our hap-py hearts will quiv-er With the mel-o-dy of peace.

CHORUS.

Yes, we'll gath-er at the riv-er; The beautiful, the beautiful riv-er—

Gather with the saints at the riv-er, That flows by the throne of God.

No. 26 Mine, Mine, Mine

Harmony by Mrs. Olive Roesink

Copyright, 1941, by the Boone Publishing Co.

Unknown

Mine, mine, mine Je-sus is mine, Mine when I'm wea-ry; mine when

Mine, Mine, Mine

I'm cheer-y. Mine, mine, mine, Jesus is mine; Je-sus is mine all the time.

No. 27 Let the King of Glory Reign

Copyright, 1938, by The Boone Publishing Co.

Harmony by MRS. EDWARD BOONE   EDWARD BOONE

Lively

1. Let the King of glo-ry reign within your heart; Let Him have His way, let Him
2. Let the King of glo-ry reign within your heart; With His matchless grace, in the
3. Let the King of glo-ry reign within your heart; He will dwell with-in keep-ing
4. Let the King of glo-ry reign within your heart; He was cru-ci-fied, and for

have full sway; His love and peace He quick-ly will im-part; Let the
rough dark place, He'll take you thru; He al-ways does His part, Let the
you from sin, All doubt and fear then quick-ly will de-part; Let the
you has died, Just yield to Him, for heav-en make a start; Let the

D. S.—Let the

Chorus

King come in to-day. Let the King, let the King, Let the
en-ter in, dwell within,

King come in to-day.

D. S.

King come in to stay, He will be your friend and will keep you to the end.

No. 28   He's Coming Back

Har. by Mrs. Edward Boone. Copyright, 1935, by Edward Boone.

Edward Boone.

1. From Mt. Ol - i - vet our Sav-iour went to Heav - en, In a cloud of glo - ry en-tered in the sky. But an an - gel spoke these words of glo-rious com - fort, In like man-ner He'll be com-ing, bye and bye.

2. Yes, He's com - ing back a - gain to take the ran-somed, To a home, He's now pre-par-ing up on high, So "let not your heart be troubled," said the Mas - ter, You'll be ris - ing when you hear the trumpet's cry. He's com-ing

3. For a thou-sand years this earth will have no tempt - er, And we'll reign down here with Je - sus on the throne, Then the wild - er - ness shall blos - som as the rose bed, Back to Pal - es-tine the Jews be gathered home.

4. Then the li - on and the lamb be sweet-ly play - ing And the curse be lift - ed too, for - ev - er more, U - ni - ver - sal peace be flow-ing like a riv - er, And His righteousness will go from shore to shore.

CHORUS.

He's com - ing back,............... a - gain to reign,............... The prom-ise
He's com - ing back   a - gain to reign,

is........... I'll come a - gain, ...''For if I go a-
the prom-ise is   I'll come a - gain,

Dedicated to the Rev. Nathan C. Beskin's Prophetic Bible Conference, held at
The First Pilgrim Tabernacle, Grand Rapids, Michigan, Jan. 3 to 20 1935

He's Coming Back

way," said Je-sus, "I'll come back for you a-gain,"....back for you a-gain.

29

I Shall Be Like Him.

Rev. W. A. SPENCER, D. D.

1. When I shall reach the more ex-cellent glory, And all my tri-als are passed,
2. We shall not wait till the glorious dawning Breaks on the vision so fair,
3. More and more like Him, repeat the blest story, O-ver and o-ver a-gain,

I shall behold Him, O won-der-ful sto-ry! I shall be like Him at last.
Now we may welcome the heavenly morning, Now we His image may bear.
Changed by His spirit from glo-ry to glo-ry, I shall be sat-is-fied then.

CHORUS.

I shall be like Him, I shall be like Him And in His beauty shall snine,

I shall be like Him, wondrously like Him, Je-sus my Sav-ior di-vine.

No. 30　The Work for Christ Our King

Copyright, 1938, by The Boone Publishing Co.

Harmony by Mrs. Edward Boone　　　　　　　　　Edward Boone

1. There's a work that we must do down here be-low If the lost and err-ing ones our
2. There is pleas-ure in the serv-ice of the King; Great reward in heaven it will
3. There are mil-lions who have nev-er heard of Him Who can save the soul from ev'ry

Christ would know. We must tell of right-eous-ness, of the peace and bless-ed-ness
sure - ly bring. What a joy for us to meet those we led to Je-sus' feet;
guilt and sin; They are waiting for the light That will make their black hearts white,

In the Sav-ior ev'ry-where we go.
'Twill be worth to us most ev-'ry-thing.
That will give them joy and peace with-in.

Chorus

Spread-ing the Gos-pel of our

Sav - ior in-to ev'-'ry land, Tell-ing the sto-ry of His grace that

is so great and grand, Cheer-ing the lost from day to day, tell-ing them

The Work for Christ Our King

there's a bet-ter way Is the task that ev-'ry-one must do for Je - sus.

Let us then be bus - y in the work of love; Stars within our crown we then shall

have a-bove; Bring to ev'ry nation full and free salvation is our work for Christ our King.

No. 31 A Charge to Keep I Have

Charles Wesley

Lowell Mason

1. A charge to keep I have, A God to glo - ri - fy,
2. To serve the pres - ent age, My call - ing to ful - fill,—
3. Arm me with jeal - ous care, As in Thy sight to live;
4. Help me to watch and pray, And on Thy - self re - ly,

A nev - er - dy - ing soul to save, And fit it for the sky.
Oh, may it all my pow'rs en - gage To do my Mas - ter's will.
And, oh, Thy serv-ant, Lord, pre - pare A strict ac - count to give.
As-sured, if I may trust be - tray, I shall for - ev - er die.

Christ Receiveth Sinful Men.

Arr. from Neumaster, 1671.   James McGranahan.

1. Sin - ners Je - sus will re - ceive: Sound this word of grace to all
2. Come, and He will give you rest; Trust Him for His word is plain;
3. Now my heart con - demns me not, Pure be - fore the law I stand;
4. Christ re - ceiv - eth sin - ful men, E - ven me with all my sin;

Who the heav'n - ly path - way leave, All who lin - ger, all who fall.
He will take the sin - ful - est; Christ re - ceiv - eth sin - ful men.
He who cleans'd me from all spot, Sat - is - fied its last de - mand.
Purg'd from ev - 'ry spot and stain, Heav'n with Him I en - ter in.

REFRAIN.

Sing it o'er............... and o'er a - gain;......... Christ re -
Sing it o'er a - gain,   Sing it o'er a - gain:

ceiv - - - eth sin - ful men;....... Make the mes - - - sage
ceiv-eth sin - ful men, Christ re - ceiveth sin-ful men;   Make the message plain,

clear and plain:........... Christ re - ceiv - eth sin - ful men.
Make the message plain:

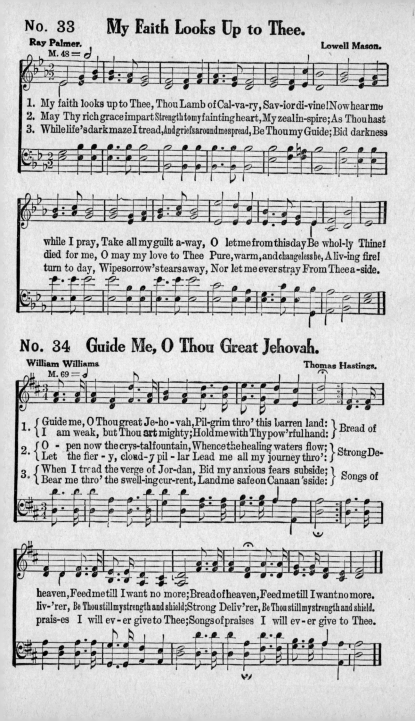

No. 33 My Faith Looks Up to Thee.

Ray Palmer.   Lowell Mason.

M. 48 = ♩

1. My faith looks up to Thee, Thou Lamb of Cal-va-ry, Sav-ior di-vine! Now hear me
2. May Thy rich grace impart Strength to my fainting heart, My zeal in-spire; As Thou hast
3. While life's dark maze I tread, And griefs around me spread, Be Thou my Guide; Bid darkness

while I pray, Take all my guilt a-way, O let me from this day Be whol-ly Thine!
died for me, O may my love to Thee Pure, warm, and changeless be, A liv-ing fire!
turn to day, Wipe sorrow's tears away, Nor let me ever stray From Thee a-side.

No. 34 Guide Me, O Thou Great Jehovah.

William Williams.   Thomas Hastings.

M. 69 = ♩

1. { Guide me, O Thou great Je-ho-vah, Pil-grim thro' this barren land:
     I am weak, but Thou art mighty; Hold me with Thy pow'rful hand: } Bread of

2. { O - pen now the crys-tal fountain, Whence the healing waters flow;
     Let the fier - y, cloud-y pil - lar Lead me all my journey thro': } Strong De-

3. { When I tread the verge of Jor-dan, Bid my anxious fears subside;
     Bear me thro' the swell-ing cur-rent, Land me safe on Canaan 's side: } Songs of

heaven, Feed me till I want no more; Bread of heaven, Feed me till I want no more.
liv-'rer, Be Thou still my strength and shield; Strong Deliv'rer, Be Thou still my strength and shield.
prais-es I will ev - er give to Thee; Songs of praises I will ev - er give to Thee.

No. 35   *Grace Sufficient*

Mrs. Justin Lindley   Edward Boone

1. How of - ten when sor-rows o'er take me As my ach-ing heart voic-es
2. When loved ones have left me heart-broken On the shore of that sad tide-
3. When down in the val - ley of shad- ow And the beck- on-ing Home-lights

my plea, I hear in sweet tones His sure prom- ise, "My grace is suf-
less sea, I still hear His ten - der voice say - ing, "My grace is suf-
I see, I hear His voice say - ing so gen - tly, "My grace is suf-

Chorus

fi - cient for thee." Oh, Sav- ior, dear Sav- ior, Thy foot - prints have

marked out the path- way for me; There come to my heart
the path-way for me;

words of com - fort, "My grace is suf - fi -cient for thee."
suf - fi -cient for thee."

Will Jesus Find Us Watching?

Fanny J. Crosby.

W. H. Doane.

1. When Je - sus comes to re - ward His serv - ants, Wheth-er it be
2. If at the dawn of the ear - ly morn - ing, He shall call us
3. Have we been true to the trust He left us? Do we seek to
4. Bless - ed are those whom the Lord finds watch-ing, In His glo - ry

noon or night, Faith - ful to Him will He find us watch-ing,
one by one, When to the Lord we re - store our tal - ents,
do our best? If in our hearts there is naught con-demns us,
they shall share; If He shall come at the dawn or mid-night,

rit.

REFRAIN.

With our lamps all trimm'd and bright?
Will He an - swer thee, "Well done?"   Oh, can we say we are
We shall have a glo - rious rest.
Will He find us watch - ing there?

read - y, broth - er? Read - y for the soul's bright home? Say, will He find

you and me still watch-ing, Wait - ing, wait-ing when the Lord shall come?

By permission.

Wonderful Peace

W. D. Cornell, alt.

W. G. Cooper

1. Far a-way in the depths of my spir-it to-night Rolls a mel-o-dy sweet-er than psalm; In ce-les-tial-like strains it un-ceas-ing-ly falls O'er my soul like an in-fi-nite calm.
2. What a treas-ure I have in this won-der-ful peace, Bur-ied deep in the heart of my soul, So se-cure that no pow-er can mine it a-way, While the years of e-ter-ni-ty roll!
3. I am rest-ing to-night in this won-der-ful peace, Rest-ing sweet-ly in Je-sus' con-trol; For I'm kept from all dan-ger by night and by day, And His glo-ry is flood-ing my soul!
4. And me-thinks when I rise to that cit-y of peace, Where the Au-thor of peace I shall see, That one strain of the song which the ran-somed will sing In that heav-en-ly king-dom will be:
5. Ah, soul! are you here with-out com-fort and rest, March-ing down the rough path-way of time? Make Je-sus your Friend ere the shad-ows grow dark; O ac-cept of this peace so sub-lime!

CHORUS

Peace, peace, won-der-ful peace, Coming down from the Fa-ther a-bove! Sweep o-ver my spir-it for-ev-er, I pray, In fath-om-less bil-lows of love!

Power in the Blood.

J. H. W.

Rev. J. H. WEBER.

1. There is pow'r in the blood, now, to wash your soul, There is pow'r in the
2. There is pow'r in the blood to make you white, There is pow'r in the
3. There is pow'r in the blood, it's a-ton-ing grace, There is pow'r in the
4. There is pow'r in the blood, plunge beneath its wave, There is pow'r in the

blood to keep you whole, There is pow'r in the blood to help you win,
blood to keep you right, There is pow'r in the blood to lead you on,
blood for all the race, There is pow'r in the blood, just look on high,
blood to keep and save, There is pow'r in the blood, be firm and true,

CHORUS.

There is pow'r in the blood to save from sin.
There is pow'r in the blood of God's dear Son. Glo-ry to the Lamb,
There is pow'r in the blood, 'tis draw-ing nigh.
There is pow'r in the blood to help, yes, you.

Glo-ry to the Lamb, for He shed His blood for thee, He will keep you

Repeat ad lib.

in the way and will nev-er let you stray, There is pow'r in the blood.

39 I Am Under The Blood.

Copyright, 1936, by The Boone Publishing Co.

Harmony by
Mrs. Edward Boone.

Edward Boone.

1. I am un-der the blood of the lamb for sin-ners slain, I am un-der the
2. I am un-der the blood like the Is - real-ite of old, It is sprinkled to -
3. I am un-der the blood, oh, how won-der-ful to know, If the an - gel of
4. I am un-der the blood, it's the on - ly safe re-treat, From the judgment and

blood shed for me; I am rest-ing in Him, while there's perfect peace within,
day on the door; There is safe - ty in-side, while the blood is there ap-plied,
death should ap-pear, He'll be pass-ing my door, for there's One who died before;
wrath soon to be; When the an - gels shall rise, pouring judgment from the skies,

CHORUS.

From my bondage and guilt I now am free. I am un-der the blood,
Though the angels of judgment o'er me soar.
It is Je - sus the One to me most dear.
To the hav-en of ref - uge I will flee.

protect-ed,

Un-der the blood, Un-der the blood of the Lamb,

safe - ly, hal-le - lu-jah, I am

Constantly a-bid-ing, safe-ly I am hiding, Un-der the blood of the Lamb.

40 Deeper, Deeper.

C. P. J.

C. P. Jones.

1. Deep-er, deep-er in the love of Je-sus Dai-ly let me go;
2. Deep-er, deep-er! bless-ed Ho-ly Spir-it, Take me deep-er still,
3. Deep-er, deep-er! tho' it cost hard tri-als, Deep-er let me go!
4. Deep-er, high-er, ev-'ry day in Je-sus, Till all con-flict past,

High-er, high-er in the school of wis-dom, More of grace to know.
Till my life is whol-ly lost in Je-sus, And his per-fect will.
Root-ed in the ho-ly love of Je-sus, Let me fruit-ful grow.
Finds me conqu'ror, and in his own im-age Per-fect-ed at last.

CHORUS.

O deep - - er yet, I pray,.............. And
O deep-er yet, I pray,   deep-er yet, I pray, And

high - er ev-'ry day,.......... And wis - - - er,
high-er ev-'ry day,   high-er ev-'ry day, And wis-er, bless-ed Lord,

bless-ed Lord,............ In thy pre-cious, ho-ly word.
.wis-er, bless-ed Lord.

No. 41 I AM DETERMINED TO HOLD OUT.

C. S. and T. P. H.

C. S. and T. P. HAMILTON.

1. When I first found Je-sus some-thing o'er me stole, Like lightning it went
2. Sa - tan, he was an-gry, said he'd soon be back, Just let the path get
3. This old-time re - lig-ion makes me sometimes shout, I don't have time to
4. When I hear the trum-pet sounding in the sky, And see the mountains

through me, and glo - ry filled my soul; Sal - va - tion made me hap - py and
nar - row, and he will lose the track; But I'm so full of glo - ry, my
gos - sip nor a - ny time to pout; They say that I'm too noi - sy, but
trem - bling, to heav - en I will fly; For Je - sus will be call - ing, there'll

took my fears a - way, And when I meet old Sa - tan to him I al-ways say:
Lord I al-ways find, And I just say to Sa - tan, "Old man, get thee be-hind."
when these blessings flow, I shout, O hal - le - lu - jah, I want the world to know.
be no time to mend, With joy I'll go up sing-ing, "I've held out to the end."

CHORUS.

"I am de - ter-mined to hold out to the end, Je - sus is with me, on

"Him I can de - pend, And I know I have sal - va - tion, for I

I Am Determined to Hold Out

feel it in my soul, I am de-ter-mined to hold out to the end."

No. 42 Clinging to Jesus, Alone

E. E. Hewitt, Alt.

M. L. McPhail

1. "Glory to Je-sus!" my glad heart sings, Je-sus a-lone, Je-sus a-lone;
2. He is my Star thro' the gloom-y night, Je-sus a-lone, Je-sus a-lone,
3. He is my strength when temptations throng, Je-sus a-lone, Je-sus a-lone,
4. All thro' the jour-ney my song shall be, Je-sus a-lone, Je-sus a-lone;

Grace and sal-va-tion to me He brings, And I am His chosen, His own.
And my chief Joy when the skies are bright; I'm clinging to Je-sus a-lone.
And tho the con-flict be hard and long, I'm cling-ing to Je-sus a-lone.
Chant-ing life's mu-sic to love's sweet key, And clinging to Je-sus a-lone.

Chorus

I will sing prais-es to Him I love; Is He not all my own?

I will press on to the home a-bove, Cling-ing to Je-sus a-lone.

No. 43   It Is Well With My Soul.

H. G. SPAFFORD.   COPYRIGHT, 1904, BY THE JOHN CHURCH CO.   P. P. BLISS.

1. When peace like a riv - er at - tend - eth my way, When
2. Though Sa - tan should buf - fet, tho' tri - als should come, Let
3. My sin— oh, the bliss of this glo - ri - ous tho't— My
4. And, Lord, haste the day when the faith shall be sight, The

sor - rows like sea - bil - lows roll, What-ev - er my lot, Thou hast
this blest as - sur - ance con - trol, That Christ hath re-gard - ed my
sin — not in part but the whole,—Is nailed to His cross, and I
clouds be roll'd back as a scroll, The trump shall re-sound, and the

taught me to say: "It is well, it is well with my soul."
help - less es - tate, And hath shed His own blood for my soul.
bear it no more; Praise the Lord, praise the Lord, O my soul!
Lord shall de-scend,—"E - ven so"— it is well with my soul.

CHORUS.

It is well ...... with my soul, ... It is well, it is well with my soul!

It is well   with my soul,

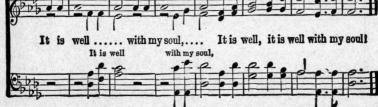

The Home Over There.

D. W. C. Huntington.

Tullius C. O'Kane.

M. 96 = ♩

1. O think of the home o-ver there, By the side of the riv - er of light,
2. O think of the friends o-ver there, Who be-fore us the journey have trod,
3. My Sav-ior is now o-ver there, There my kindred and friends are at rest,
4. I'll soon be at home o-ver there, For the end of my jour-ney I see;

over there,

Where the saints, all immortal and fair, Are robed in their garments of white.
Of the songs that they breathe on the air, In their home in the pal-ace of God.
Then a-way from my sor-row and care, Let me fly to the land of the blest.
Man - y dear to my heart, o-ver there, Are watching and waiting for me.

over there.

REFRAIN.

O-ver there, o - ver there,

O think of the home o-ver there;
O think of the friends o-ver there;
My Sav-ior is now o-ver there;
Over there, over there, I'll soon be at home o-ver there;

over there;

O-ver there, o-ver there, o-ver there,

O think of the home o-ver there.
O think of the friends o-ver there.
My Sav-ior is now o-ver there.
Over there, over there, I'll soon be at home o-ver there.

The Bloodwashed Pilgrim

Anon.

1. I saw a blood-washed pil grim, A sin - ner saved by grace,
2. I saw him in the fur - nace; He doubt - ed not, nor feared,
3. 'Mid storms, and clouds, and tri - als, In pris - on, at the stake,
4. I saw him o - ver - com - ing, Thro' all the swell - ing strife,

Up - on the King's great high - way With peace - ful, shin - ing face;
And in the flames be - side him The Son of God ap - peared;
He leaped for joy, re - joic - ing, 'Twas all for Je - sus' sake;
Un - til he crossed the thresh-old Of God's E - ter - nal Life;

Temp-ta - tions sore be - set him, But noth - ing could af - fright;
Tho' sev - en times 'twas heat - ed With all the tempt-er's might,
That God should count him worth - y, Was such su - preme de - light,
The Crown, the Throne, the Scep - tre, The Name, the Stone so White,

He said, "The yoke is eas - y, The bur - den, it is light."
He said, "The yoke is eas - y, The bur - den, it is light."
He cried, "The yoke is eas - y, The bur - den is so light."
Were his, who found, in Je - sus, The yoke and bur - den light.

CHORUS.

Then palms of vic - to-ry, crowns of glo - ry, Palms of vic - to-ry I shall wear.

No. 46 My Burdens Rolled Away.

COPYRIGHT, 1907, BY I. G. MARTIN.

M. A. S.

Mrs. Minnie A. Steele.

1. I re-mem-ber when my burdens rolled a-way, I had car-ried them for years night and day; When I sought the blessed Lord, and I took him at his word, Then at once all my bur-dens rolled a - way.

2. I re-mem-ber where my burdens rolled a-way, That I feared would nev-er leave night or day; Je - sus showed to me the loss, so I left them at the cross, I was glad when my bur-dens rolled a - way.

3. I re-mem-ber why my burdens rolled a-way, That had hindered me for years night and day; As I sought the throne of grace, just a glimpse of Je-sus' face, And I knew that my bur-dens rolled a - way.

4. I am sing-ing since my burdens rolled a-way, There's a song with-in my heart night and day; I am liv - ing for my King, and with joy I shout and sing Hal-le-lu-jah! all my bur-dens rolled a - way.

CHORUS.

Rolled away, rolled a-way, I am happy since my burdens rolled a-way; Rolled a-way, rolled a-way, I am hap - py since my burdens rolled a - way.

Rolled away, rolled a-way, since my burdens rolled a - way; Rolled a - way, rolled a-way,

No. 47. Wonderful Words of Life.

P. P. Bliss.   P. P. Bliss.

1. Sing them o-ver a-gain to me, Won-der-ful words of Life;
2. Christ, the bless-ed One, gives 'to all, Won-der-ful words of Life;
3. Sweet-ly ech-o the gos-pel call, Won-der-ful words of Life;

Let me more of their beau-ty see, Won-der-ful words of Life;
Sin-ner, list to the lov-ing call, Won-der-ful words of Life;
Of-fer par-don and peace to all, Won-der-ful words of Life;

Words of life and beau-ty, Teach me faith and du-ty.
All so free-ly giv-en, Woo-ing us to heav-en.
Je-sus, on-ly Sav-ior, Sanc-ti-fy for-ev-er.

CHORUS.

Beau-ti-ful words, won-der-ful words, Won-der-ful words of Life;

Beau-ti-ful words, won-der-ful words, Won-der-ful words of Life.

The Lily of the Valley.

J. R. MURRAY.

ARR. by THORO HARRIS.

1. I've found a friend in Je-sus, He's ev-'ry-thing to me, He's the fairest of ten
2. He all my griefs has tak-en, and all my sorrows borne; In temp-ta-tion He's my
3. He'll nev-er, nev-er leave me, nor yet forsake me here, While I live by faith and

thousand to my soul; The Lil-y of the Val-ley in Him a-lone I see All I
strong and mighty tow'r; I've all for Him forsaken, I've all my idols torn From my
do His bless-ed will; A wall of fire about me, I've nothing now to fear; With His

need to cleanse and make me fully whole. In sorrow He's my comfort, in trouble He's my
heart, and now He keeps me by His pow'r. Tho' all the world forsake me, and Satan tempts me
manna He my hungry soul shall fill; Then sweeping up to glory, we'll see His blessed

CHORUS.—*In sorrow He's my comfort, in trouble He's my*

stay, He tells me ev-'ry care on Him to roll. Hallelujah! He's the Lil-y of the
sore, Thru Je-sus I shall safely reach the goal. He's the Lil-y of the
face, Where rivers of delight shall ev-er roll. He's the Lil-y of the

stay; He tells me ev-'ry care on Him to roll. (Hallelujah!) He's the Lil-y of the

D. S

Valley, the bright and morning Star, He's the fairest of ten thousand to my soul.

Valley, the bright and morning Star, He's the fairest of ten thousand to my soul.

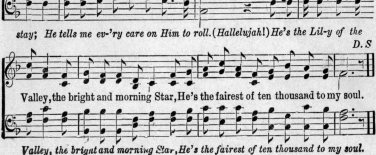

No. 49 Altogether Lovely

Mrs. Justin Lindley Copyright, 1941, by The Boone Publishing Co. **Mrs. Olive Roesink**
Trio

1. He's al-to-geth-er love-ly, the fair-est of the fair; His righteous
2. His lead-ings I'll not ques-tion, He knows the way be-fore; His ten-der-
3. He speaks, His love is changeless, it makes my heart rejoice; I hear in

hand up-holds me, I'm safe with-in His care. En-joy-ing full-est
ness and mer-cy shall broken hearts re-store. His grace is all suf-
si-lent rap-ture the beauty of His voice; In lov-ing ad-o-

par-don, His ben-e-dic-tion mine, In ab-so-lute de-vo-tion, I
fi-cient, His joy and peace so free; The path He bids me fol-low is
ra-tion my tro-phies I then bring, A-dor-ing His bright kingdom, and

Chorus

yield to Christ di-vine.
al-ways best for me. He's al-to-geth-er love-ly; The fair-est
crown Him King of Kings.

of the fair. His gracious love sustains me; I'm safe with-in His care.

Follow On.

W. O. Cushing.

Robert Lowry.

M. 80

1. Down in the val-ley with my Sav-ior I would go, Where the flow'rs are
2. Down in the val-ley with my Sav-ior I would go, Where the storms are
3. Down in the val-ley, or up-on the mountain steep, Close be-side my

bloom-ing and the sweet wa-ters flow; Ev-'ry-where He leads me I would
sweep-ing and the dark wa-ters flow; With His hand to lead me I will
Sav-ior would my soul ev-er keep; He will lead me safe-ly in the

FINE.

fol-low, fol-low on, Walk-ing in His foot-steps till the crown be won.
nev-er, nev-er fear, Dan-ger can-not fright me if my Lord is near.
path that He has trod, Up to where they gath-er on the hills of God.

D.S.—Ev-'ry-where He leads me I would fol-low on!

REFRAIN.

Fol-low! fol-low! I would fol-low Je-sus! An-y-where, ev-'ry-where,

D. S.

I would fol-low on! Fol-low! fol-low! I would fol-low Je-sus!

No. 51 SUNLIGHT.

J. W. Van De Venter.

W. S. Weeden.

1. I wandered in the shades of night, Till Je-sus came to me,
2. Though clouds may gather in the sky, And billows round me roll,
3. While walking in the light of God, I, sweet communion find;
4. I cross the wide ex-tended fields, I journey o'er the plain,
5. Soon I shall see Him as He is, The Light that came to me,

And with the sun-light of His love Bade all my darkness flee.
How-ev-er dark the world may be I've sun-light in my soul.
I press with ho-ly vig-or on And leave the world behind.
And in the sun-light of His love I reap the gold-en grain.
Be-hold the brightness of His face, Throughout e-ter-ni-ty.

CHORUS

Sun-light, sun-light, in my soul to-day, Sunlight, sunlight,
to-day, yes,

all a-long the way, Since the Sav-iour found me,
nar-row way,

took away my sin, I have had the sunlight of His love within.
load of sin,

Copyright, by Weeden & Van De Venter. Used by per.

No. 52. Beulah Land.

BY PERMISSION OF MRS. JNO. R. SWENEY.

Edgar Page.   Jno. R. Sweney.

1. I've reached the land of corn and wine, And all its rich-es free-ly mine;
2. My Sav-ior comes and walks with me, And sweet communion here have we;
3. A sweet per-fume up-on the breeze Is borne from ev-er-ver-nal trees,
4. The zeph-yrs seem to float to me Sweet sounds of heav-en's mel-o-dy,

Here shines undimmed one bliss-ful day, For all my night has passed a-way.
He gen-tly leads me by His hand, For this is heav-en's bor-der-land.
And flow'rs, that nev-er-fad-ing grow Where streams of life for-ev-er flow.
As an-gels with the white-robed throng Join in the sweet re-demp-tion song.

CHORUS.

O Beu-lah Land, sweet Beu-lah Land, As on thy high-est mount I stand,

I look a-way a-cross the sea, Where mansions are pre-pared for me,

And view the shin-ing glo-ry-shore,—My heav'n, my home for-ev-er more!

No. 53   He Abides.

Herbert Buffum.   Owned by God's Bible School   D. M. Shanks.

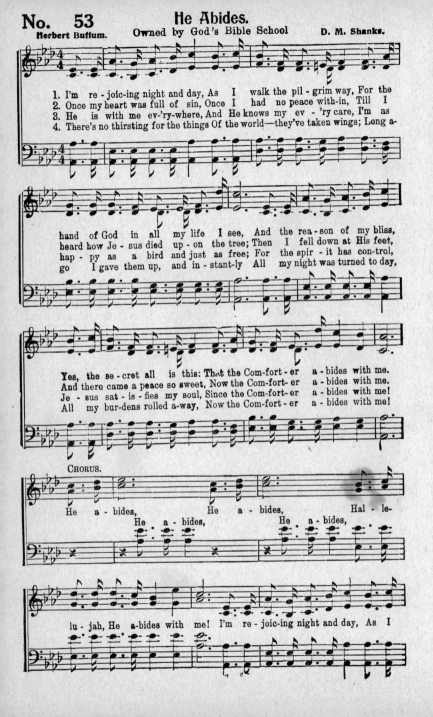

1. I'm re-joic-ing night and day, As I walk the pil-grim way, For the
2. Once my heart was full of sin, Once I had no peace with-in, Till I
3. He is with me ev-'ry-where, And He knows my ev-'ry care, I'm as
4. There's no thirsting for the things Of the world—they've taken wings; Long a-

hand of God in all my life I see, And the rea-son of my bliss,
heard how Je-sus died up-on the tree; Then I fell down at His feet,
hap-py as a bird and just as free; For the spir-it has con-trol,
go I gave them up, and in-stant-ly All my night was turned to day,

Yes, the se-cret all is this: That the Com-fort-er a-bides with me.
And there came a peace so sweet, Now the Com-fort-er a-bides with me.
Je-sus sat-is-fies my soul, Since the Com-fort-er a-bides with me!
All my bur-dens rolled a-way, Now the Com-fort-er a-bides with me!

CHORUS.

He a-bides, He a-bides, Hal-le-
He a-bides, He a-bides,

lu-jah, He a-bides with me! I'm re-joic-ing night and day, As I

He Abides

walk the nar-row way, For the Com-fort-er a-bides with me.

54 The Hidden Treasures

Mrs. Justin Lindley

Edward Boone

1. Search-ing as for hid-den treas-ure, Seek-ing as for pur-est gold,
2. It will lead to heights of rap-ture Where I hear glad voic-es ring;
3. I can see the man-y man-sions, With their glo-ries bright and fair,

While I read the sa-cred pag-es, Truths of val-ue there un-fold.
'Tis an-gel-ic choirs of heav-en, And they crown our Sav-iour, King.
And their shin-ing tow'rs of splen-dor; One is wait-ing for me there.

Chorus

Oh, the height, the depth, the full-ness Of the love of God to men,

Of His hand that guides so safe-ly, Of re-demp-tion's per-fect plan.

No. 55 — My Redeemer.

P. P. Bliss. James McGranahan.

M. 72 = ♩.

1. I will sing of my Re-deem-er, And His won-drous love to me;
2. I will tell the won-drous sto-ry, How my lost es-tate to save,
3. I will praise my dear Re-deem-er, His tri-um-phant pow'r I'll tell,
4. I will sing of my Re-deem-er, And His heav'n-ly love to me;

On the cru-el cross He suf-fered, From the curse to set me free.
In His boundless love and mer-cy, He the ran-som free-ly gave.
How the vic-to-ry He giv-eth O-ver sin, and death, and hell.
He from death to life hath brought me, Son of God with Him to be.

CHORUS.

Sing, oh, sing.......... of my Re-deem-er, With His
Sing, oh, sing of my Re-deem-er, Sing, oh, sing of my Re-deem-er,

blood....... He purchased me,....... On the cross..... He sealed my
He purchased me, With His blood He purchased me, He sealed my pardon, On the

Repeat pp after last verse.

par - don, Paid the debt........ and made me free........
cross He sealed my pardon, Paid the debt and made me free, and made me free.

No. 56 I Know I Love Thee Better, Lord.

Frances R. Havergal. Copyright, 1918, by R. E. Hudson. Renewal. R. E. Hudson.

1. I know I love Thee better, Lord, Than any earthly joy;
2. I know that Thou art nearer still Than any earthly throng;
3. Thou hast put gladness in my heart; Then may I well be glad!
4. O Savior, precious Savior mine! What will Thy presence be,

For Thou hast given me the peace Which nothing can destroy.
And sweeter is the tho't of Thee Than any lovely song.
Without the secret of Thy love I could not but be sad.
If such a life of joy can crown Our walk on earth with Thee?

CHORUS.

The half has never yet been told,
yet been told,
Of love so full and free!

rit.........

The half has never yet been told,
yet been told,
The blood—it cleanseth me!
cleanseth me!

Wonderful Love

Mrs. Justin Lindley   Copyright, 1941, by The Boone Publishing Co.   Edward Boone

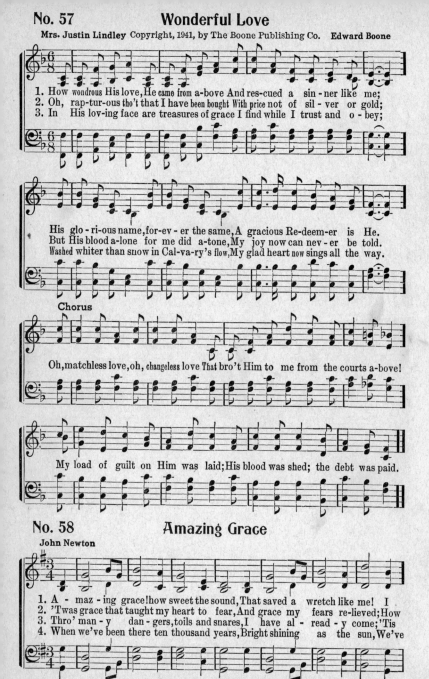

1. How wondrous His love, He came from a-bove And res-cued a sin-ner like me;
2. Oh, rap-tur-ous tho't that I have been bought With price not of sil-ver or gold;
3. In His lov-ing face are treasures of grace I find while I trust and o-bey;

His glo-ri-ous name, for-ev-er the same, A gracious Re-deem-er is He.
But His blood a-lone for me did a-tone, My joy now can nev-er be told.
Washed whiter than snow in Cal-va-ry's flow, My glad heart now sings all the way.

Chorus

Oh, matchless love, oh, changeless love That bro't Him to me from the courts a-bove!

My load of guilt on Him was laid; His blood was shed; the debt was paid.

Amazing Grace

John Newton

1. A - maz - ing grace! how sweet the sound, That saved a wretch like me! I
2. 'Twas grace that taught my heart to fear, And grace my fears re-lieved; How
3. Thro' man - y dan - gers, toils and snares, I have al - read - y come; 'Tis
4. When we've been there ten thousand years, Bright shining as the sun, We've

Amazing Grace

once was lost, but now am found, Was blind, but now I see.
pre - cious did that grace ap - pear The hour I first be - lieved!
grace hath bro't me safe thus far, And grace will lead me home.
no less days to sing God's praise Than when we first be - gun.

59

He'll Understand

To K. G. Lawrence

D. M. S.

COPYRIGHT, 1922, BY GOD'S BIBLE SCHOOL

D. M. Shanks

1. If your bur-dens heav-y grow, Tell it to Je-sus, He'll un-der-stand;
2. If you need a help-er kind, Tell it to Je-sus, He'll un-der-stand;
3. When the tempt-er press-es sore, Tell it to Je-sus, He'll un-der-stand;
4. When you reach the Jor-dan tide, Tell it to Je-sus, He'll un-der-stand;

All your sor - row He doth know, Tell it to Je-sus, He'll un-der-stand.
Bet - ter friend you'll nev-er find, Tell it to Je-sus, He'll un-der-stand.
He has passed this way be - fore, Tell it to Je-sus, He'll un-der-stand.
He'll be stand-ing near your side, Tell it to Je-sus, He'll un-der-stand.

CHORUS

Tell it to Je-sus, He'll un-der-stand, Burdens will leave you at His com-mand;

While you hold His guid-ing hand, Tell it to Je-sus, He'll un-der-stand.

60 Ye Must Be Born Again

W. T. Sleeper

Geo. C. Stebbins

1. A rul-er once came to Je-sus by night, To ask Him the
2. Ye chil-dren of men, at-tend to the word, So sol-emn-ly
3. Oh, ye who would en-ter that glo-ri-ous rest, And sing with the
4. A dear one in heav-en thy heart yearns to see, At the beau-ti-ful

way of sal-va-tion and light; The Master made an-swer in words true and plain,
ut-tered by Je-sus, the Lord; And let not this mes-sage to you be in vain,
ransomed the song of the blest; The life ev-er-last-ing if ye would ob-tain,
gate may be watching for thee; Then list to the note of this sol-emn re-frain,

CHORUS

"Ye must be born a-gain."...... "Ye must be born a-
a-gain.

gain,"...... "Ye must be born a-gain;".... I ver-i-ly,
a-gain,   a-gain;

ver-i-ly, say un-to thee, "Ye must be born a-gain."....
a-gain.

61 Nothing But the Blood.

R. L.

Robert Lowry.

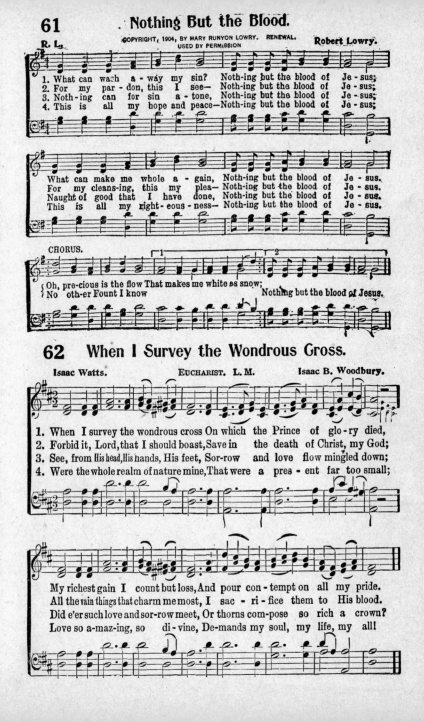

1. What can wash a-way my sin? Noth-ing but the blood of Je-sus;
2. For my par-don, this I see— Noth-ing but the blood of Je-sus;
3. Noth-ing can for sin a-tone, Noth-ing but the blood of Je-sus;
4. This is all my hope and peace— Noth-ing but the blood of Je-sus;

What can make me whole a-gain, Noth-ing but the blood of Je-sus.
For my cleans-ing, this my plea— Noth-ing but the blood of Je-sus.
Naught of good that I have done, Noth-ing but the blood of Je-sus.
This is all my right-eous-ness— Noth-ing but the blood of Je-sus.

CHORUS.

Oh, pre-cious is the flow That makes me white as snow;
No oth-er Fount I know

Nothing but the blood of Jesus.

62 When I Survey the Wondrous Cross.

Isaac Watts.

EUCHARIST. L. M.

Isaac B. Woodbury.

1. When I survey the wondrous cross On which the Prince of glo-ry died,
2. Forbid it, Lord, that I should boast, Save in the death of Christ, my God;
3. See, from His head, His hands, His feet, Sor-row and love flow min-gled down;
4. Were the whole realm of nature mine, That were a pres-ent far too small;

My richest gain I count but loss, And pour con-tempt on all my pride.
All the vain things that charm me most, I sac-ri-fice them to His blood.
Did e'er such love and sor-row meet, Or thorns com-pose so rich a crown?
Love so a-maz-ing, so di-vine, De-mands my soul, my life, my all!

No. 63   An Old Account Settled.

F. M. G.   F. M. Graham.

1. There was a time on earth When in the book of heav'n An old account was standing For sins yet un-for-giv'n; My name was at the top, And man-y things be-low, I went un-to the Keep-er, And settled long a-go.

2. The old account was large, And growing ev-'ry day, For I was al-ways sin-ning, And nev-er tried to pay; But when I looked a-head And saw such pain and woe, I said that I would set-tle, And settled long a-go.

3. When at the judgment bar I stand be-fore my King, And He the book will o-pen, He can-not find a thing; Then will my heart be glad, While tears of joy will flow Be-cause I had it set-tled, And settled long a-go.

4. O sin-ner, seek the Lord, Re-pent of all your sin, For thus He has com-mand-ed, If you would en-ter in; And then if you should live A hundred years be-low, E'en here you'll not re-gret it, You settled long a-go.

CHORUS.

Long a-go, Long a-go, Yes, the old account was set-tled long a-go; And the record's clear to-day, For He

Down on my knees, I set-tled it all,

Hal-le-lu-jah!

An Old Account Settled.

Washed my sins a-way, When the old account was settled long a-go.

No. 64 Are You Washed in the Blood?

E. A. H.

BY PERMISSION.

Rev. E. A. Hoffman.

M. 104

1. Have you been to Je-sus for the cleansing pow'r? Are you washed in the
2. Are you walk-ing dai-ly by the Sav-ior's side? Are you washed in the
3. When the Bridegroom cometh will your robes be white, Pure and white in the
4. Lay a - side the garments that are stained with sin, And be washed in the

blood of the Lamb? Are you full - y trusting in His grace this hour? Are you
blood of the Lamb? Do you rest each moment in the Cru - ci - fied? Are you
blood of the Lamb? Will your soul be ready for the mansions bright, And be
blood of the Lamb; There's a fountain flowing for the soul un-clean, Oh, be

D.S.—*Are your garments spotless? Are they white as snow? Are you*

FINE. CHORUS.

washed in the blood of the Lamb? Are you washed in the
washed in the blood of the Lamb?

Are you washed

D. S.

blood, In the soul-cleansing blood of the Lamb?
in the blood, of the Lamb?

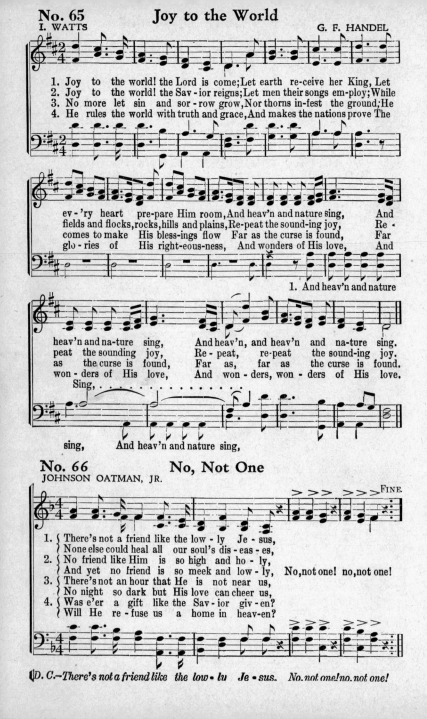

No. 65   Joy to the World

I. WATTS   G. F. HANDEL

1. Joy to the world! the Lord is come; Let earth re-ceive her King, Let
2. Joy to the world! the Sav-ior reigns; Let men their songs em-ploy; While
3. No more let sin and sor-row grow, Nor thorns in-fest the ground; He
4. He rules the world with truth and grace, And makes the nations prove The

ev-'ry heart pre-pare Him room, And heav'n and nature sing, And
fields and flocks, rocks, hills and plains, Re-peat the sound-ing joy, Re-
comes to make His bless-ings flow Far as the curse is found, Far
glo-ries of His right-eous-ness, And wonders of His love, And

1. And heav'n and nature

heav'n and na-ture sing, And heav'n, and heav'n and na-ture sing.
peat the sounding joy, Re - peat, re-peat the sound-ing joy.
as the curse is found, Far as, far as the curse is found.
won-ders of His love, And won - ders, won - ders of His love.
Sing, ...

sing, And heav'n and nature sing,

No. 66   No, Not One

JOHNSON OATMAN, JR.   FINE.

1. { There's not a friend like the low - ly Je - sus,
     None else could heal all our soul's dis - eas - es,
2. { No friend like Him is so high and ho - ly,
     And yet no friend is so meek and low - ly, No, not one! no, not one!
3. { There's not an hour that He is not near us,
     No night so dark but His love can cheer us,
4. { Was e'er a gift like the Sav - ior giv - en?
     Will He re - fuse us a home in heav-en?

D. C.—There's not a friend like the low-ly Je - sus. No, not one! no, not one!

No, Not One. Concluded.

CHORUS.

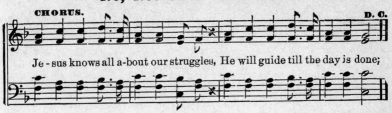

Je - sus knows all a-bout our struggles, He will guide till the day is done;

No. 67 All Hail the Power of Jesus' Name.

EDWARD PERRONET.   OLIVER HOLDEN.

1. All hail the pow'r of Je - sus' name! Let an - gels pros-trate fall;
2. Crown Him, ye martyrs of our God, Who from His al - tar call;
3. Ye chos-en seed of Is - rael's race, Ye ran-somed from the fall;
4. Sin - ner, whose love can ne'er for - get The worm-wood and the gall;
5. Let ev - 'ry kin-dred, ev - 'ry tribe, On this ter - res-trial ball,
6. Oh, that with yon-der sa - cred throng We at His feet may fall;

Bring forth the roy - al di - a - dem, And crown Him Lord of all;
Ex - tol the stem of Jes - se's rod, And crown Him Lord of all;
Hail Him who saves you by His grace, And crown Him Lord of all;
Go, spread your trophies at His feet, And crown Him Lord of all;
To Him all maj - es - ty as-cribe, And crown Him Lord of all;
We'll join the ev - er - last - ing song, And crown Him Lord of all;

Bring forth the roy - al di - a - dem, And crown Him Lord of all.
Ex - tol the stem of Jes - se's rod, And crown Him Lord of all.
Hail Him who saves you by His grace, And crown Him Lord of all.
Go, spread your trophies at His feet, And crown Him Lord of all.
To Him all maj - es - ty as-cribe, And crown Him Lord of all.
We'll join the ev - er - last - ing song, And crown Him Lord of all.

Standing on the Promises.

"The word of the Lord endureth forever."—1 Peter 1: 25.

R. K. C.   R. KELSO CARTER.

1. Standing on the promis- es of Christ, my King, Thro' e-ter- nal a - ges
2. Standing on the promis- es that can - not fail, When the howling storms of
3. Standing on the promis- es I now can see, Perfect, present cleansing
4. Standing on the promis- es of Christ the Lord, Bound to Him e -ter-nal-
5. Standing on the promis- es I can - not fall, List'ning ev-'ry moment

let His prais-es ring; Glory in the highest, I will shout and sing,
doubt and fear as - sail, By the liv-ing word of God I shall pre - vail,
in the blood for me; Standing in the lib - er - ty where Christ makes free,
ly by love's strong chord, O- ver-coming dai- ly with the Spir -it's sword,
to the Spir- it's call, Rest -ing in my Sav-iour as my all in all,

CHORUS.

Standing on the promises of God. Stand - ing,   stand - ing,
Standing on the promises, Standing on the promises,

Standing on the promises of God my Sav -iour, Stand - ing,
Standing on the prom-is-es,

stand - - ing,   I'm standing on the prom-is - es of God.
Stand- ing on the prom - is - es,

69 Tell Me the Story of Jesus.

Fanny J. Crosby.

Jno. R. Sweney.

1. Tell me the sto-ry of Je-sus, Write on my heart ev-'ry word;
2. Fast-ing a-lone in the des-ert, Tell of the days that are passed,
3. Tell of the cross where they nailed Him, Writh-ing in an-guish and pain;

CHO.—*Tell me the sto-ry of Je-sus, Write on my heart ev-'ry word;*

FINE.

Tell me the sto-ry most pre-cious, Sweet-est that ev-er was heard.
How for our sins He was tempt-ed, Yet was tri-um-phant at last.
Tell of the grave where they laid Him, Tell how He liv-eth a-gain.

Tell me the sto-ry most pre-cious, Sweet-est that ev-er was heard.

Tell how the an-gels, in cho-rus, Sang as they wel-comed His birth,
Tell of the years of His la-bor, Tell of the sor-row He bore,
Love in that sto-ry so ten-der, Clear-er than ev-er I see;

D.C. for Cho.

"Glo-ry to God in the high-est! Peace and good ti-dings to earth,"
He was de-spised and af-flict-ed, Home-less, re-ject-ed and poor.
Stay, let me weep while you whis-per, Love paid the ran-som for me.

The above song recorded on RAINBOW RECORDS

No. 70   "Then We Shall Rise"

Copyright, 1937, by The Boone Publishing Co.

Har. by MRS. EDWARD BOONE   EDWARD BOONE

1. Soon our Lord is com-ing back as He has prom-ised, To gath - er all the
2. In the Bi - ble we are told that He is com - ing, As light-ning flash-ing
3. It is lik-ened to a thief that comes at midnight, So un - ex - pect - ed
4. Then the Lord Himself will come to meet the ransomed, He'll let no oth - er

saints up in the air; In a twink-ling of an eye we'll all be leav - ing,
forth from east to west; He will gath - er all the righteous that are liv - ing,
will the Lord appear; So be watching lest the Lord should find you sleep-ing,
per - son fill His place; Just as I-saac met Re - bec - ca in the meadow,

For the glor-ious mar-riage supper o - ver there. (yes, over there)
And u - nite them with the dead so long at rest. (so long at rest) Then we shall
Oh, be read - y for His com-ing draweth near. (yes, draweth near)
So in mid - air we will meet Him face to face. (Him face to face)

CHORUS

rise   Up t'ward the skies................ to meet our
   Yes, we shall rise   Up t'ward the skies,

Sav - iour in the air................ Oh what a
bless - ed lov - ing Sav-iour with the saints up in the air,

"Then We Shall Rise"

No. 71 I Know Whom I Have Believed

COPYRIGHT, 1913, BY HALL-MACK CO.
INTERNATIONAL COPYRIGHT SECURED

C. A. M.   C. Austin Miles

1. Prais-es be to God, for I am glo-ry bound, For I am a
2. I am un-der grace, nor long-er un-der law, In the bless-ed
3. When the days are drear-y, spent in pain or woe, When the watches
4. Not a-lone for me, but all who will may find Sweet-est con-so-

mir-a-cle of grace; Ask of God a sign, it sure-ly can be found
light of love I'm free; To the word of God I go when sore distrest,
of the night are long, I'll be trust-ing Je-sus, so in ev-'ry place
la-tion for his woe; Seek the will of God, and for the word of Christ

CHORUS.

In a hap-py Chris-tian's face.
This is what it says to me; "I know whom I have be-
I can al-ways sing this song;
To the bless-ed Bi-ble go.

liev-ed and am per-suad-ed that he is a-ble to keep that which I've com-

mit-ted un-to him a-gainst that day." O praise the Lord!

72. Our Lord's Return to Earth Again.

J. M. K.   Acts 1: 9, 10, 11.   J. M. KIRK.

1. I am watch-ing for the com-ing of the glad mil-len-nial day,
2. Je-sus' com-ing back will be the an-swer to earth's sorrowing cry,
3. Yes, the ran-somed of the Lord shall come to Zi-on then with joy,
4. Then the sin and sor-row, pain and death of this dark world shall cease,

When our blessed Lord shall come and catch his wait-ing Bride a-way; Oh! my
For the knowledge of the Lord shall fill the earth and sea and sky; God shall
And in all his ho-ly mountain nothing hurts or shall de-stroy; Per-fect
In a glorious reign with Je-sus of a thousand years of peace; All the

heart is fill'd with rapt-ure as I la-bor, watch and pray, For the Lord is coming
take a-way all sickness and the suff'rer's tears will dry, When our Saviour shall come
peace shall reign in ev-'ry heart, and love with-out al-loy, Aft-er Jesus shall come
earth is groaning, cry-ing for that day of sweet re-lease, For our Je-sus to come

D. S.—*will be bound a thousand years, we'll have no tempter then, Aft-er Jesus shall come*

FINE.   CHORUS.

back to earth a-gain. Oh! our Lord is com-ing back to earth a-gain,
is com-ing back to earth a-gain,

back to earth a-gain.

D. S.

Yes, our Lord is com-ing back to earth a-gain; Sa-tan
is com-ing back to earth a-gain,

Lost But Found

three verses by
rd Boone

Unknown

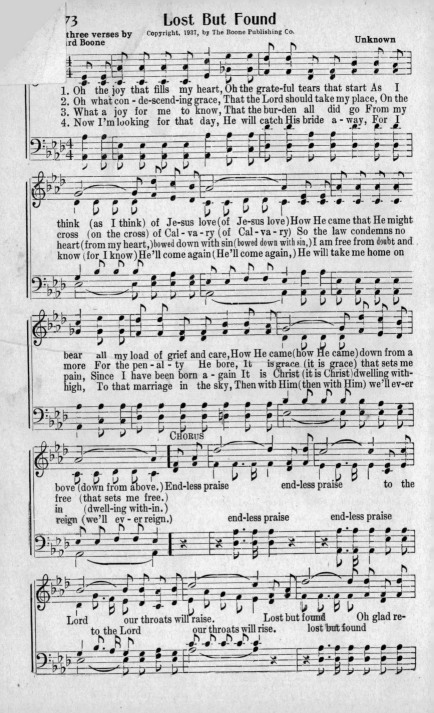

1. Oh the joy that fills my heart, Oh the grate-ful tears that start As I
2. Oh what con - de-scend-ing grace, That the Lord should take my place, On the
3. What a joy for me to know, That the bur-den all did go From my
4. Now I'm looking for that day, He will catch His bride a - way, For I

think (as I think) of Je-sus love (of Je-sus love) How He came that He might
cross (on the cross) of Cal - va - ry (of Cal-va-ry) So the law condemns no
heart (from my heart,) bowed down with sin (bowed down with sin,) I am free from doubt and
know (for I know) He'll come again (He'll come again,) He will take me home on

bear all my load of grief and care, How He came (how He came) down from a
more For the pen - al - ty He bore, It is grace (it is grace) that sets me
pain, Since I have been born a - gain It is Christ (it is Christ) dwelling with-
high, To that marriage in the sky, Then with Him (then with Him) we'll ev-er

CHORUS

bove (down from above.) End-less praise   end-less praise   to the
free (that sets me free.)
in (dwell-ing with-in.)
reign (we'll ev - er reign.)   end-less praise   end-less praise

Lord   our throats will raise.   Lost but found   Oh glad re-
    to the Lord   our throats will rise.   lost but found

Lost But Found

frain   Dead but now   I live a-gain.
oh, glad re-frain   dead but now   I live a-gain.

No. 74   The Hills Of Grace

Mrs. Justin Lindley Copyright, 1941, by The Boone Publishing Co.   **Edward Boone**

Duet

1. The hills of grace, so fair to see; From path-ways dim they
2. On hills of grace no clouds a-rise, With dark-ness black to
3. The love-ly hills where flow-ers bloom, In balm-y air, with

beck-on me. They tow'r above all doubt and fear, Bright hills of grace with Jesus near.
veil the skies, The sun-lit days are calm and bright; These loft-y hills yield pure delight.
rich per-fume, A bliss-ful place with breath so rare, On hills of grace sweet peace is there.

Chorus

Oh, shin-ing hills, fair hills of grace, Where light of dawn reveals His face, Where

hearts are free and joy-notes ring, And His redeemed with rap-ture sing.

Never Alone!

"I will not leave you comfortless."—John 14: 18

1. I've seen the light-ning flash-ing, And heard the thun-der roll,
2. The world's fierce winds are blow-ing; Temp-ta-tion sharp and keen;
3. When in af-flic-tion's val-ley I tread the road of care,
4. He died on Cal-v'ry's moun-tain, For me they pierced His side,

I've felt sin's break-ers dash-ing, Which al-most con-quered my soul;
I have a peace in know-ing My Sav-iour stands be-tween—
My Sav-iour helps me car-ry The cross so heav-y to bear;
For me He o-pened that foun-tain, The crim-son, cleans-ing tide;

I've heard the voice of my Sav-iour Bid-ding me still to fight on;
He stands to shield me from dan-ger When my friends are all gone;
Tho' all a-round me is dark-ness, Earth-ly joys all flown;
For me He wait-eth in glo-ry, Seat-ed up-on His throne;

He prom-ised nev-er to leave me, Nev-er to leave me a-lone!
He prom-ised nev-er to leave me, Nev-er to leave me a-lone!
My Sav-iour whis-pers His prom-ise, Nev-er to leave me a-lone!
He prom-ised nev-er to leave me, Nev-er to leave me a-lone!

REFRAIN

No, nev-er a-lone! No, nev-er a-lone! He promised nev-er to leave me,

Never Alone!

Nev-er to leave me a-lone! Nev-er to leave me a-lone!

76   A Shelter in the Time of Storm

Vernon J. Charlesworth
Arr. by Ira D. Sankey

Ira D. Sankey

1. The Lord's our Rock, in Him we hide, A shel-ter in the time of storm;
2. A shade by day, de-fense by night, A shel-ter in the time of storm;
3. The rag-ing storms may round us beat, A shel-ter in the time of storm;
4. O Rock di-vine, O Ref-uge dear, A shel-ter in the time of storm;

Se-cure what-ev-er ill be-tide, A shel-ter in the time of storm.
No fears a-larm, no foes af-fright, A shel-ter in the time of storm.
We'll nev-er leave our safe re-treat, A shel-ter in the time of storm.
Be Thou our help-er ev-er near, A shel-ter in the time of storm.

CHORUS

Oh, Je-sus is a Rock in a wea-ry land, A wea-ry land, a wea-ry land;

Oh, Je-sus is a Rock in a wea-ry land, A shel-ter in the time of storm.

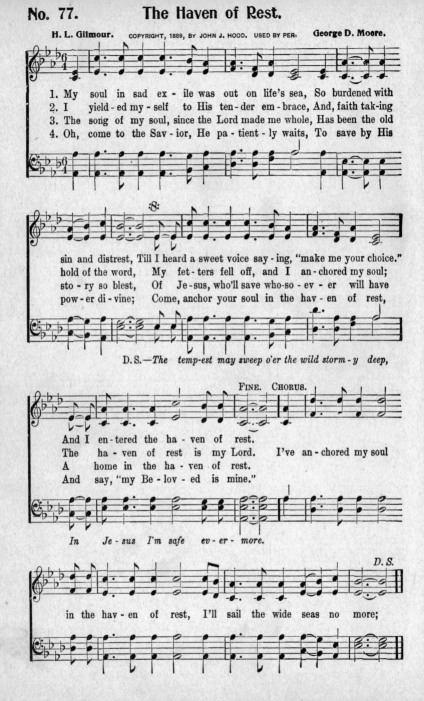

No. 77. The Haven of Rest.

H. L. Gilmour. COPYRIGHT, 1889, BY JOHN J. HOOD. USED BY PER. George D. Moore.

1. My soul in sad ex - ile was out on life's sea, So burdened with
2. I yield - ed my - self to His ten - der em - brace, And, faith tak-ing
3. The song of my soul, since the Lord made me whole, Has been the old
4. Oh, come to the Sav - ior, He pa - tient - ly waits, To save by His

sin and distrest, Till I heard a sweet voice say - ing, "make me your choice."
hold of the word, My fet - ters fell off, and I an - chored my soul;
sto - ry so blest, Of Je - sus, who'll save who - so - ev - er will have
pow - er di - vine; Come, anchor your soul in the hav - en of rest,

D. S.—The temp-est may sweep o'er the wild storm - y deep,

FINE. CHORUS.

And I en - tered the ha - ven of rest.
The ha - ven of rest is my Lord. I've an - chored my soul
A home in the ha - ven of rest.
And say, "my Be - lov - ed is mine."

In Je - sus I'm safe ev - er - more.

D. S.

in the hav - en of rest, I'll sail the wide seas no more;

No. 78

Where He Leads Me.

E. W. Blandly.

Arranged.

M. 80 = 𝅘𝅥

1. I can hear my Sav - ior call-ing, I can hear my Sav - ior call-ing,
2. I'll go with Him thro' the gar-den, I'll go with Him thro' the gar-den,
3. I'll go with Him thro' the judgment, I'll go with Him thro' the judg-ment,
4. He will give me grace and glo - ry, He will give me grace and glo - ry,

Cho.–*Where He leads me I will fol-low, Where He leads me I will fol - low,*

ad lib.

D. C.

I can hear my Sav - ior call-ing, "Take My cross and follow, fol - low Me."
I'll go with Him thro' the gar-den, I'll go with Him, with Him all the way.
I'll go with Him thro' the judgment, I'll go with Him, with Him all the way.
He will give me grace and glo - ry, And go with me, with me all the way.

Where He leads me I will fol - low, I'll go with Him, with Him all the way.

No. 79

I'll Live For Him.

R. E. Hudson.

COPYRIGHT, 1918, BY R. E. HUDSON. RENEWAL.

C. R. Dunbar.

M. 76 = 𝅘𝅥

1. My life, my love, I give to Thee, Thou Lamb of God, who died for me;
2. I now be-lieve Thou dost re-ceive, For Thou hast died that I might live;
3. O Thou who died on Cal-va - ry To save my soul and make me free,

Cho.–*I'll live for Him who died for me, How hap - py then my life shall be!*

D C. Chorus.

Oh, may I ev - er faith - ful be, My Sav - ior and my God!
And now hence-forth I'll trust in Thee, My Sav - ior and my God!
I'll con - se-crate my life to Thee, My Sav - ior and my God!

I'll live for Him who died for me, My Sav - ior and my God!

No. 80. We Have an Anchor.

Priscilla J. Owens.

Wm. J. Kirkpatrick.

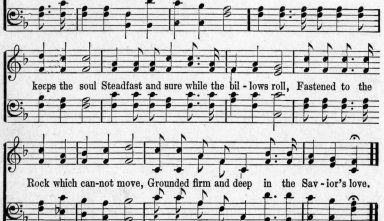

1. Will your an-chor hold in the storms of life, When the clouds un-
2. It is safe-ly moored, 'twill the storm withstand, For 'tis well se-
3. It will firm-ly hold in the straits of fear, When the break-ers
4. It will sure-ly hold in the floods of death, When the wa-ters
5. When our eyes be-hold thro' the gath-'ring night The cit-y of

fold their wings of strife? When the strong tides lift, and the ca-bles strain,
cured by the Sav-ior's hand; And the ca-bles, passed from His heart to mine,
have told the reef is near, Tho' the tempest rave and the wild winds blow,
cold chill our la-test breath, On the ris-ing tide it can nev-er fail,
gold, our har-bor bright, We shall an-chor fast by the heav'nly shore,

REFRAIN.

Will your an-chor drift, or firm re-main?
Can de-fy the blast, thro' strength di-vine.
Not an an-gry wave shall our bark o'erflow. We have an an-chor that
While our hopes a-bide with-in the veil.
With the storms all past for-ev-er-more.

keeps the soul Steadfast and sure while the bil-lows roll, Fastened to the

Rock which can-not move, Grounded firm and deep in the Sav-ior's love.

81 I Have Chosen You

Mrs. Justin Lindley   Edward Boone

1. When on the field of con-flict, I find this prom-ise true;
2. When shad-ows dark sur-round me, He gives me strength a - new;
3. These pre-cious words of prom-ise Changed not thro' pass-ing years;

It brings new grace for tri - als—"Fear not, I've cho - sen you."
"Fear not," He speaks so gen - tly, "For I have cho - sen you."
At last, the jour-ney end - ed, He'll wipe a - way all tears.

CHORUS

"Fear not, fear not," He speaks these words of com-fort, "Fear not, fear not;"

He cheers and takes me through. I hear Him say, "I am thy God, I

know the path that you have trod; I........ have cho-sen you."
yes, I

No. 82 — I am Thine, O Lord.

F. J. Crosby.

W. H. Doane.

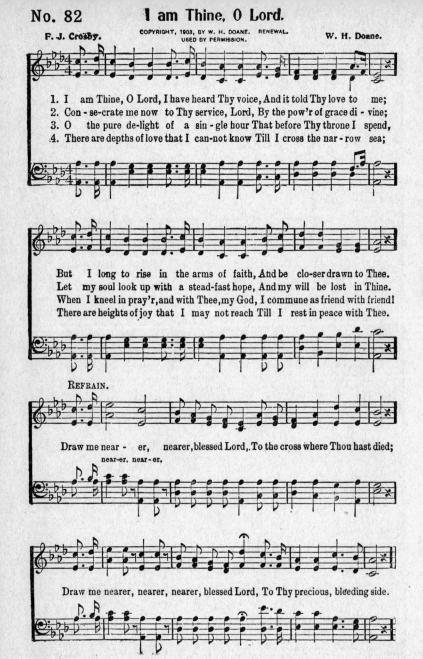

1. I am Thine, O Lord, I have heard Thy voice, And it told Thy love to me;
2. Con - se - crate me now to Thy service, Lord, By the pow'r of grace di - vine;
3. O the pure de-light of a sin - gle hour That before Thy throne I spend,
4. There are depths of love that I can-not know Till I cross the nar - row sea;

But I long to rise in the arms of faith, And be clo-ser drawn to Thee.
Let my soul look up with a stead-fast hope, And my will be lost in Thine.
When I kneel in pray'r, and with Thee, my God, I commune as friend with friend!
There are heights of joy that I may not reach Till I rest in peace with Thee.

REFRAIN.

Draw me near - er, nearer, blessed Lord, To the cross where Thou hast died;
near-er, near-er,

Draw me nearer, nearer, nearer, blessed Lord, To Thy precious, bleeding side.

No. 83   Where He Leads I'll Follow.

W. A. O.   COPYRIGHT, 1885, BY W. A. OGDEN.   W. A. Ogden.

1. Sweet are the prom-is-es, Kind is the word; Dear-er far than
2. Sweet is the ten-der love Je-sus hath shown, Sweet-er far than
3. List to His lov-ing words, "Come un-to me!" Wear-y, heav-y-

an-y mes-sage man ev-er heard; Pure was the mind of Christ,
an-y love that mor-tals have known; Kind to the err-ing one,
lad-en, there is sweet rest for thee; Trust in His prom-is-es,

Sin-less, I see; He the great ex-am-ple is, and pat-tern for me.
Faith-ful is He; He the great ex-am-ple is, and pat-tern for me.
Faith-ful and sure; Lean up-on the Sav-ior, and thy soul is se-cure.

CHORUS.

Where . . . . He leads I'll fol - - - low,
Where He leads I'll fol-low,   Where He leads I'll fol-low,

1.
Fol - - low all the way;
Fol-low all the way, yes, fol-low all the way;

2.
Follow Jesus ev-'ry day.

84 Victory Ahead.

W. G.

Rev. William Grum.

1. When the hosts of Is - ra- el, led by God, Round the walls of Jer - i - cho
2. Dav - id, with a shepherd's sling and five stones, Met the gi - ant on the field
3. Dan - iel pray'd un - to the Lord thrice each day, Then un-to the li - on's den
4. Of - ten with the carnal mind I was tried, Ask-ing for de-liv- er - ance
5. When like those who've gone before to that land, By death's river cold and dark

firm - ly trod; Trusting in the Lord, they felt the conq'ror's tread, By faith they
all a - lone; Trusting in the Lord, he knew what God had said, By faith he
led the way; Trusting in the Lord, he did not fear nor dread, By faith he
oft I cried; Trusting in the Lord, I reck-oned I was dead, By faith I
I may stand; Trusting in the Lord, I will not fear nor dread, By faith I

Chorus.

saw the vic - to - ry a - head.
saw the vic - to - ry a - head.
saw the vic - to - ry a - head. Vic - to-ry a-head! Vic - to-ry a - head!
saw the vic - to - ry a - head.
see the vic - to - ry a - head.

Thro' the blood of Je - sus, Vic - to - ry a - head; Trust-ing in the Lord, I

feel the conq'ror's tread, By faith I see the vic to - ry a - head!

No. 85   When We All Get to Heaven.

E. E. Hewitt.   **Mrs. J. G. Wilson.**

1. Sing the won-drous love of Je-sus, Sing His mer-cy and His grace;
2. While we walk the pil-grim path-way, Clouds will o-ver-spread the sky;
3. Let us then be true and faith-ful, Trust-ing, serv-ing ev-'ry day;
4. On-ward to the prize be-fore us! Soon His beau-ty we'll be-hold;

In the mansions, bright and bless-ed, He'll pre-pare for us a place.
But when trav'ling days are o-ver, Not a shad-ow, not a sigh.
Just one glimpse of Him in glo-ry Will the toils of life re-pay.
Soon the pearl-y gates will o-pen, We shall tread the streets of gold.

for us a place.

CHORUS.

When we all get to heav-en, What a day of re-
When we all   What a

joic-ing that will be!   When we all   see
day of re-joic-ing that will be!   When we all

Je-sus, We'll sing and shout the vic-to-ry..............
and   shout the vic-to-ry.

Beauty for Ashes

J. G. C.

J. G. Crabbe

1. I sing the love of God, my Fa - ther, Whose Spir - it a - bides with - in,
2. I sing the love of God, my Sav - ior, Who suf - fered up - on the tree,
3. I sing the beau - ty of the Gos - pel That scat - ters, not thorns, but flow'rs,

Who chang - es all my grief to glad - ness, And par - dons me all my sin.
That, in the se - cret of His pres - ence, My bond - age might freedom be.
That bids me scat - ter smiles and sunbeams Wher - ev - er are lone - ly hours.

Tho' clouds may low - er, dark and drear - y, Yet He has promised to be near;
He comes "to bind the brok - en - heart - ed;" He comes the fainting soul to cheer;
The "gar - ment of His praise" it of - fers For "heav - i - ness of spir - it" drear;

He gives me sun - shine for my shad - ow, And "beau - ty for ash - es," here.
He gives me "oil of joy" for morn - ing, And "beau - ty for ash - es," here.
It gives me sun - shine for my shad - ow, And "beau - ty for ash - es," here.

D.S.—gives me sunshine for my shad - ow, And "beau - ty for ash - es," here.

Chorus

He gives me joy . . . . in place of sor - - - - row;
He gives me joy in place of care;

Beauty for Ashes

D. S.

He gives me love............... that casts out fear; He

He gives me love that casts out fear;

No. 87 Make Me a Blessing To-day

Rev. H. C. Zelley

H. L. Gilmour

1. I do not ask to choose my path, Lord, lead me in Thy way;
2. A-round me, Lord, are sin-ful men, Who scorn and dis-o-bey;
3. To those who once Thy love have known, But now are far a-stray,
4. Some saints of Thine are in dis-tress, And for de-liv-'rance pray;
5. What-ev-er er-rand Thou hast, Lord, Send me, and I'll o-bey;

Inspire each tho't and prompt each word And make me a bless-ing to-day.
Use me to win them from their sins And make me a bless-ing to-day.
Help me to win them back to Thee, And make me a bless-ing to-day.
O let me go and help them, Lord, And make me a bless-ing to-day.
Use me in an-y way Thou wilt, And make me a bless-ing to-day.

Chorus

Bless me, Lord, and make me a bless-ing, I'll glad-ly Thy message con-vey;

Use me to help some poor needy soul, And make me a blessing to-day.

No. 88 Close to Thee.

Fanny J. Crosby.

S. J. Vail.

M. 80 = ♩

1. Thou my ev-er-last-ing por-tion, More than friend or life to me,
2. Not for ease or world-ly pleas-ure, Nor for fame my prayer shall be;
3. Lead me thro' the vale of shad-ows, Bear me o'er life's fit-ful sea:

FINE.

All a-long my pil-grim jour-ney, Sav-ior, let me walk with Thee.
Glad-ly will I toil and suf-fer, On-ly let me walk with Thee.
Then the gate of life e-ter-nal, May I en-ter, Lord, with Thee.

D.S.—All a-long my pil-grim jour-ney, Sav-ior, let me walk with Thee.
D.S.—Glad-ly will I toil and suf-fer, On-ly let me walk with Thee.
D.S.—Then the gate of life e-ter-nal, May I en-ter, Lord, with Thee.

REFRAIN.

D. S.

1-3. Close to Thee, close to Thee, Close to Thee, close to Thee;

No. 89 Jesus, Savior, Pilot Me.

Edward Hopper.

J. E. Gould.

M. 80 = ♩

FINE.

1. Je-sus, Sav-ior, pi-lot me O-ver life's tem-pes-tuous sea;
D.C.—Chart and com-pass came from Thee; Je-sus, Sav-ior, pi-lot me.
2. As a moth-er stills her child, Thou canst hush the o-cean wild;
D.C.—Won-drous Sov-'reign of the sea, Je-sus, Sav-ior, pi-lot me.
3. When at last I near the shore, And the fear-ful break-ers roar
D.C.—May I hear Thee say to me, "Fear not, I will pi-lot Thee."

Jesus, Savior, Pilot Me.

D. C.

Un-known waves a-round me roll, Hid-ing rocks and treach-'rous shoal;
Boist'rous waves o-bey Thy will When Thou say'st to them "Be still!"
'Twixt me and the peace-ful rest, Then, while lean-ing on Thy breast,

No. 90

Love Divine.

Charles Wesley.

John Zundel.

M. 92 =

1. Love di-vine, all love ex-cell-ing, Joy of heav'n, to earth come down;

FINE.

Fix in us Thy hum-ble dwell-ing, All Thy faith-ful mer-cies crown:
D.S.—Vis-it us with Thy sal-va-tion, En-ter ev-'ry trem-bling heart.

D. S.

Je-sus, Thou art all com-pas-sion, Pure, un-bound-ed love Thou art;

2 Breathe, O breathe Thy loving Spirit
  Into every troubled breast!
Let us all in Thee inherit,
  Let us find that second rest.
Take away the love of sinning;
  Alpha and Omega be;
End of faith, as its beginning,
  Set our hearts at liberty.

3 Come, Almighty to deliver,
  Let us all Thy grace receive;
Suddenly return, and never,
  Never more Thy temples leave:
Thee we would be always blessing,
  Serve Thee as Thy hosts above,
Pray, and praise Thee without ceasing,
  Glory in Thy perfect love.

Have a Little Talk With Him

Mrs. Evelyn Scott

Edward Boone

1. A little talk with Je-sus, it smooths the rug-ged road And heals the
2. You suf-fer pain and an-guish; your load-ed down with care And liv-ing
3. If you are sore-ly tempt-ed to leave the nar-row way, The Son of
4. Let's wait a lit-tle lon-ger till His ap-point-ed day; Let's glo-ry

wound-ed spir-it, much light-er makes the load. You trav-el on life's
ev-'ry mo-ment in dark-ness or de-spair. Thru all these man-y
God, your High Priest, each day for you does pray. He knows a-bout your
in the knowl-edge that Je-sus is the way. So do not be dis-

jour-ney a-midst the toil and sin; Re-mem-ber ev-'ry prom-ise,
tri-als your Sav-ior too has been: Go tell Him all a-bout it,
weak-ness a-bout sur-round-ing sin; He'll help you in each tri-al,
cour-aged, keep look-ing up! not in— Re-mem-ber ev-'ry prom-ise,

CHORUS

have a lit-tle talk with Him. A lit-tle talk with Him, a lit-tle talk with

Him, Just tell Him all a-bout it, Have a lit-tle talk with Him.

He Brought Me Out

Rev. H. J. Zelley. Chorus by H. L. G. H. L. Gilmour.

1. My heart was distress'd 'neath Jehovah's dread frown, And low in the
2. He placed me up-on the strong Rock by His side, My steps were es-
3. He gave me a song, 'twas a new song of praise, By day and by
4. I'll sing of His won-der-ful mer-cy to me, I'll praise Him till

pit where my sins dragg'd me down; I cried to the Lord from the
tab-lished and here I'll a-bide; No dan-ger of fall-ing while
night its sweet notes I will raise; My heart's o-ver-flow-ing, I'm
all men His good-ness shall see; I'll sing of sal-va-tion at

deep mir-y clay, Who ten-der-ly bro't me out to gold-en day.
here I re-main, But stand by His grace un-til the crown I gain.
hap-py and free, I'll praise my Re-deem-er, who has res-cued me.
home and a-broad, Till ma-ny shall hear the truth and trust in God.

Chorus.

He bro't me out of the mir-y clay, He set my feet on the Rock to stay;

He puts a song in my soul to-day, A song of praise, hal-le-lu-jah!

93   Come to the Feast.

Charlotte G. Homer.

COPYRIGHT, 1895, BY CHAS. H. GABRIEL.
W. E. M. HACKLEMAN, OWNER.

W. A. Ogden.

1. "All things are ready," come to the feast! Come, for the ta - ble now is
2. "All things are ready," come to the feast! Come, for the door is o - pen
3. "All things are ready," come to the feast! Come, while He waits to welcome
4. "All things are ready," come to the feast! Leave ev - 'ry care and world-ly

spread; Ye fam - ish - ing, ye wea - ry, come, And thou shalt be rich - ly fed.
wide; A place of hon - or is re - serv'd For [you at the Mas - ter's side.
thee; De - lay not while this day is thine, To-mor-row may nev - er be.
strife; Come, feast up - on the love of God, And drink ev - er - last-ing life.

CHORUS.

Hear .... the in - vi - ta - - tion, Come, "who - so - ev - er
Hear the in - vi - ta - tion, "Who-so-ev-er will," Hear the in - vi - ta - tion,

will;" .... Praise God .... for full sal -
"Who-so-ev - er will;" Praise God for full sal - va - tion For

va - - - - - tion For "who - so - ev - er will."
"who - so - ev - er will,"

No. 94   The Child of a King

HATTIE E. BUELL.

Arr. by Rev. JOHN B. SUMNER.

1. My Fa-ther is rich in hous-es and lands, He hold-eth the
2. My Fa-ther's own Son, the Sav-ior of men, Once wander'd o'er
3. I once was an out-cast stranger on earth, A sin-ner by
4. A tent or a cot-tage, why should I care? They're building a

wealth of the world in His hands! Of ru-bies and diamonds, of
earth as the poor-est of them, But now He is reign-ing for-
choice, and an al-ien by birth! But I've been a-dopt-ed, my
pal-ace for me o-ver there! Tho' ex-iled from home, yet

sil-ver and gold, His cof-fers are full,—He has rich-es un-told.
ev-er on high, And will give me a home in heav'n by and by.
name's written down, An heir to a man-sion, a robe, and a crown.
still I may sing: All glo-ry to God, I'm the child of a King.

CHORUS.

I'm the child of a King, The child of a King! With

ad lib.

Je-sus, my Sav-ior, I'm the child of a King!

Nearer, My God, to Thee.

Sarah F. Adams.

Lowell Mason.

1. Near-er, my God, to Thee, Near-er to Thee! E'en tho' it be a cross
2. Tho' like the wan-der-er, The sun gone down, Darkness be o-ver me,
3. There let the way ap-pear, Steps un-to heav'n; All that Thou sendest me,
4. Then, with my waking tho'ts Bright with Thy praise, Out of my stony griefs
5. Or if, on joy-ful wing, Cleav-ing the sky, Sun, moon and stars for-got,

D. S.—Near-er, my God, to Thee,

FINE.

D. S.

That rais-eth me; Still all my song shall be Near-er, my God, to Thee,
My rest a stone, Yet in my dreams I'd be Near-er, my God, to Thee,
In mer-cy giv'n; An-gels to beck-on me Near-er, my God, to Thee,
Beth-el I'll raise; So by my woes to be Near-er, my God, to Thee,
Up-ward I fly, Still all my song shall be Near-er, my God, to Thee,

Near-er to Thee!

Glory to His Name.

Rev. E. A. Hoffman.

Rev. J. H. Stockton.

1. Down at the cross where my Sav-ior died, Down where for cleans-
2. I am so won-drous-ly saved from sin, Je-sus so sweet-
3. O pre-cious fount-ain, that saves from sin! I am so glad-
4. Come to this fount-ain, so rich and sweet; Cast thy poor soul

ing from sin I cried; There to my heart was the blood ap-plied;
ly a-bides with-in; There at the cross where He took me in;
I have en-tered in; There Je-sus saves and keeps me clean;
at the Sav-ior's feet; Plunge in to-day, and be made com-plete;

D. S.—There to my heart was the blood ap-plied;

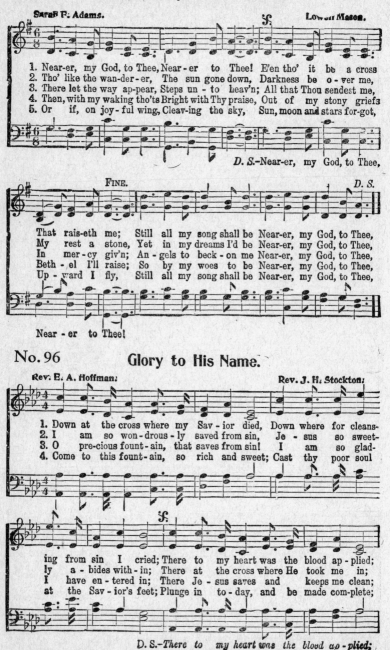

Glory to His Name:

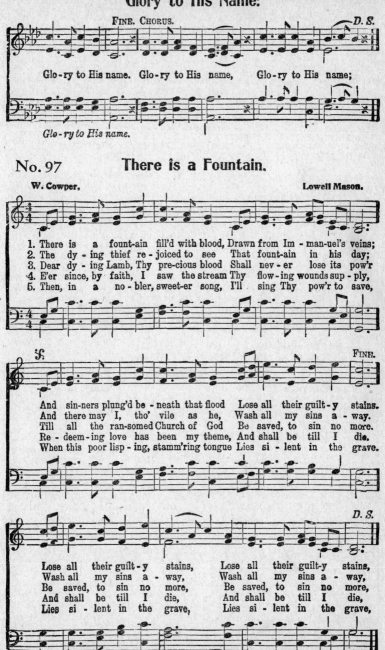

FINE. CHORUS. **D. S.**

Glo-ry to His name. Glo-ry to His name, Glo-ry to His name;

Glo-ry to His name.

No. 97 — There is a Fountain.

W. Cowper. Lowell Mason.

1. There is a fount-ain fill'd with blood, Drawn from Im-man-uel's veins;
2. The dy-ing thief re-joiced to see That fount-ain in his day;
3. Dear dy-ing Lamb, Thy pre-cious blood Shall nev-er lose its pow'r
4. E'er since, by faith, I saw the stream Thy flow-ing wounds sup-ply,
5. Then, in a no-bler, sweet-er song, I'll sing Thy pow'r to save,

D. S. **FINE.**

And sin-ners plung'd be-neath that flood Lose all their guilt-y stains.
And there may I, tho' vile as he, Wash all my sins a-way.
Till all the ran-somed Church of God Be saved, to sin no more.
Re-deem-ing love has been my theme, And shall be till I die.
When this poor lisp-ing, stamm'ring tongue Lies si-lent in the grave.

D. S.

Lose all their guilt-y stains, Lose all their guilt-y stains,
Wash all my sins a-way, Wash all my sins a-way,
Be saved, to sin no more, Be saved, to sin no more,
And shall be till I die, And shall be till I die,
Lies si-lent in the grave, Lies si-lent in the grave,

Alone With God.

Rev. Johnson Oatman, Jr.   Wm. J. Kirkpatrick.

1. When storms of life are round me beating, When rough the path that I have trod,
2. What tho' the clouds have gather'd o'er me? What tho' I've pass'd beneath the rod?
3. 'Tis there I find new strength for du-ty, As o'er the sands of time I plod,
4. And when I see the moment nearing When I shall sleep beneath the sod,

With-in my clos-et door re-treat-ing, I love to be a-lone with God.
God's perfect will there lies be-fore me, When I am thus a-lone with God.
I see the King in all his beau-ty, While resting there a-lone with God.
When time with me is dis-ap-pear-ing, I want to be a-lone with God.

CHORUS.

A-lone with God.............. the world for-bid-den, A-lone with
A - lone with God,

God,......... O blest re-treat! Alone with God,............ and in him
A-lone with God,   Alone with God,

ritard.

hid-den, To hold with him.............. com-mun-ion sweet.
To hold with him

99 Since I Have Been Redeemed.

E. O. E.   COPYRIGHT, 1912, BY E. O. EXCELL. RENEWAL.   E. O. Excell.

1. I have a song I love to sing, Since I have been re - deemed,
2. I have a Christ that sat - is - fies, Since I have been re - deemed,
3. I have a Wit - ness bright and clear, Since I have been re - deemed,
4. I have a joy I can't ex - press, Since I have been re - deemed,
5. I have a home pre-pared for me, Since I have been re - deemed,

Of my Re - deem-er, Sav - ior, King, Since I have been re-deemed.
To do His will my high - est prize, Since I have been re-deemed.
Dis - pel - ling ev - 'ry doubt and fear, Since I have been re-deemed.
All thro' His blood and right-eous - ness, Since I have been re-deemed.
Where I shall dwell e - ter - nal - ly, Since I have been re-deemed.

CHORUS.

Since I . . . . . have been redeemed,   Since I have been redeemed,
Since I have been redeemed, Since   I have been redeemed,

I will glo - ry in His name; I will glo - ry in my Sav-ior's name.

100 Wonderful.

H. L.   Haldor Lillenas.

1. O my heart sings to-day, sings for joy and glad-ness, Je-sus saves,
2. Once a slave, now I'm free, free from con-dem-na-tion, Je-sus gives
3. Liv-ing here with my Lord in a ho-ly un-ion, Day by day,

sat-is-fies, ban-ish-es my sad-ness; Guilt is gone, peace is mine,
lib-er-ty and a full sal-va-tion; Now the sins of the past
all the way hold-ing sweet com-mun-ion; O what change grace hath wrought

peace like to a riv-er, Je-sus is won-der-ful, might-y to de-liv-er.
have been all for-giv-en, And my name is inscribed on the book of heaven.
in my low-ly sta-tion! Since my soul has received full and free salva-tion.

CHORUS.

Won-der-ful, won-der-ful, Je-sus is to me, Coun-sel-or,

Prince of Peace, Might-y God is He;   Sav-ing me, keep-ing me

Sweet Hour of Prayer.

W. W. Walford.

Wm. B. Bradbury.

M. 108 =

1. Sweet hour of prayer, sweet hour of prayer, That calls me from a world of care,
2. Sweet hour of prayer, sweet hour of prayer, Thy wings shall my pe - ti - tion bear
3. Sweet hour of prayer, sweet hour of prayer, May I thy con - so - la-tion share,

FINE

And bids me, at my Father's throne, Make all my wants and wish - es known!
D.S.—And oft es-caped the tempter's snare, By thy re - turn, sweet hour of prayer.
To Him, whose truth and faith-ful-ness En-gage the wait - ing soul to bless:
D.S.—I'll cast on Him my ev - 'ry care, And wait for thee, sweet hour of prayer.
Till from Mount Pisgah's loft-y height I view my home, and take my flight;
D.S.—And shout while passing thro' the air, Fare-well, fare-well, sweet hour of prayer!

D. S.

In sea-sons of dis-tress and grief, My soul has oft - en found re - lief,
And since He bids me seek His face, Be-lieve His word, and trust His grace,
In my im-mor-tal flesh I'll rise To seize the ev - er - last - ing prize,

Blest Be the Tie.

John Fawcett.

Hans George Naegeli.

M. 84 =

1. Blest be the tie that binds Our hearts in Chris - tian love;
2. Be - fore our Fa - ther's throne, We pour our ar - dent pray'rs;
3. We share our mu - tual woes, Our mu - tual bur - dens bear;
4. When we a - sun - der part, It gives us in - ward pain;

The fel - low - ship of kin - dred minds Is like to that a - bove.
Our fears, our hopes, our aims are one, Our com-forts and our cares.
And oft - en for each oth - er flows The sym - pa - thiz-'ing tear.
But we shall still be joined in heart, And hope to meet a - gain.

No. 104　　I Need Thee Every Hour.

Mrs. Mary S. Hawks.　　　　　　　　　　　　Rev. Robert Lowry.

1. I need Thee ev-'ry hour, Most gra - cious Lord; No ten-der voice like
2. I need Thee ev-'ry hour, Stay Thou near by; Temp-ta-tions lose their
3. I need Thee ev-'ry hour, In joy or pain; Come quick-ly and a-
4. I need Thee ev-'ry hour, Most Ho - ly One; O make me Thine in-

CHORUS.

Thine Can peace af - ford.
pow'r When Thou art nigh.　　I need Thee, O I need Thee; Ev-'ry hour I
bide, Or life is vain.
deed, Thou bless-ed Son!

need Thee! O bless me now, my Sav - ior, I come to Thee!

The Solid Rock.

REFRAIN.

On Christ, the sol - id Rock I stand; All oth - er ground is sink-ing sand, All

oth - er ground is sink-ing sand.

3 His oath, His covenant, His blood
Support me in the whelming flood;
When all around my soul gives way,
He then is all my hope and stay.

4 When He shall come with trumpet sound,
Oh, may I then in Him be found;
Dressed in His righteousness alone,
Faultless to stand before the throne.

No. 107   Savior, More Than Life.

COPYRIGHT, 1906, BY W. H. DOANE.
F. T. DOANE, OWNER.

Fanny J. Crosby.

M. 69 =

W. H. Doane.

1. Sav - ior, more than life to me,   I am cling-ing, cling-ing close to Thee;
2. Thro' this chang-ing world be-low, Lead me gen-tly, gen-tly as I   go;
3. Let   me love Thee more and more, Till   this fleet-ing, fleet-ing life is   o'er;

Let   Thy pre-cious blood ap - plied, Keep me ev - er, ev - er near Thy side.
Trust-ing Thee, I can - not stray, I   can nev - er, nev - er lose my way.
Till   my soul is lost in love, In   a brighter, brighter world a - bove.

FINE.

D.S.—May Thy ten - der love to   me, Bind me   clos-er, clos-er, Lord, to Thee.

REFRAIN.

D. S.

Ev - 'ry day,   ev - 'ry hour,   Let me feel Thy cleans-ing pow'r;
Ev - 'ry day and hour, ev - 'ry day and hour,

Holy, Holy, Holy.

Reginald Heber.

John B. Dykes.

M. 92 =

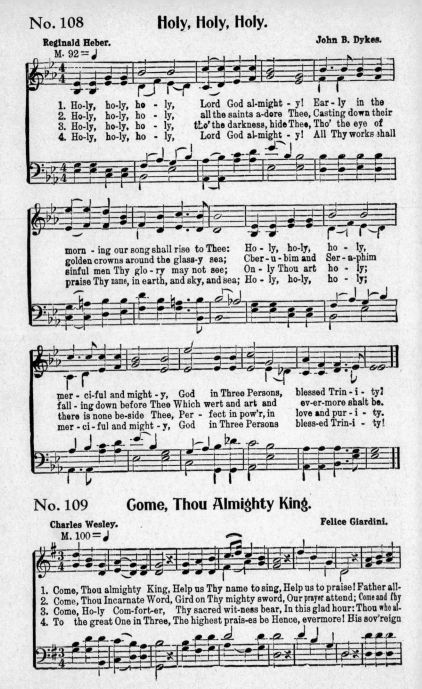

1. Ho-ly, ho-ly, ho - ly, Lord God al-might - y! Ear - ly in the
2. Ho-ly, ho-ly, ho - ly, all the saints a-dore Thee, Casting down their
3. Ho-ly, ho-ly, ho - ly, tho' the darkness, hide Thee, Tho' the eye of
4. Ho-ly, ho-ly, ho - ly, Lord God al-might - y! All Thy works shall

morn - ing our song shall rise to Thee: Ho-ly, ho-ly, ho - ly,
golden crowns around the glass-y sea; Cher - u - bim and Ser - a-phim
sinful men Thy glo - ry may not see; On - ly Thou art ho - ly;
praise Thy name, in earth, and sky, and sea; Ho - ly, ho-ly, ho - ly;

mer - ci-ful and might - y, God in Three Persons, blessed Trin - i - ty!
fall - ing down before Thee Which wert and art and ev-er-more shalt be.
there is none be-side Thee, Per - fect in pow'r, in love and pur - i - ty.
mer - ci-ful and might - y, God in Three Persons bless-ed Trin-i - ty!

No. 109

Come, Thou Almighty King.

Charles Wesley.

Felice Giardini.

M. 100 =

1. Come, Thou almighty King, Help us Thy name to sing, Help us to praise! Father all-
2. Come, Thou Incarnate Word, Gird on Thy mighty sword, Our prayer attend; Come and Thy
3. Come, Ho-ly Com-fort-er, Thy sacred wit-ness bear, In this glad hour: Thou who al-
4. To the great One in Three, The highest prais-es be Hence, evermore! His sov'reign

Come, Thou Almighty King.

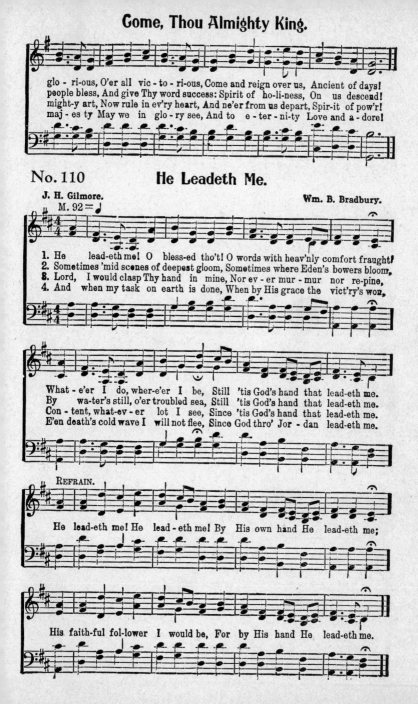

glo - ri-ous, O'er all vic - to - ri-ous, Come and reign over us, Ancient of days!
people bless, And give Thy word success: Spirit of ho-li-ness, On us descend!
might-y art, Now rule in ev'ry heart, And ne'er from us depart, Spir-it of pow'r!
maj - es ty May we in glo-ry see, And to e - ter - ni-ty Love and a - dore!

No. 110   # He Leadeth Me.

J. H. Gilmore.   Wm. B. Bradbury.

M. 92 =

1. He   lead-eth me! O   bless-ed tho't! O words with heav'nly comfort fraught!
2. Sometimes 'mid scenes of deepest gloom, Sometimes where Eden's bowers bloom,
3. Lord, I would clasp Thy hand in mine, Nor ev - er mur - mur nor re-pine,
4. And when my task on earth is done, When by His grace the vict'ry's won,

What - e'er I do, wher-e'er I be, Still 'tis God's hand that lead-eth me.
By   wa-ter's still, o'er troubled sea, Still 'tis God's hand that lead-eth me.
Con - tent, what-ev - er lot I see, Since 'tis God's hand that lead-eth me.
E'en death's cold wave I will not flee, Since God thro' Jor - dan lead-eth me.

Refrain.

He lead-eth me! He lead - eth me! By His own hand He lead-eth me;

His faith-ful fol-lower I would be, For by His hand He lead-eth me.

No. 111   Near the Cross.

Fanny J. Crosby.   USED BY PERMISSION.   W. H. Doane.

M. 50

1. Je - sus, keep me near the Cross! There a pre-cious foun-tain,
2. Near the Cross, a trem-bling soul, Love and mer-cy found me;
3. Near the Cross! O Lamb of God, Bring its scenes be - fore me;
4. Near the Cross I'll watch and wait, Hop - ing, trust-ing ev - er,

FINE

Free to all— a heal-ing stream, Flows from Cal-vary's moun-tain.
There the Bright and Morn-ing Star, Sheds its beams a - round me.
Help me walk from day to day, With its shad - ows o'er me.
Till I reach the gold - en strand, Just be-yond the riv - er.

D.S.—*Till my rap-tured soul shall find Rest be-yond the riv - er.*

CHORUS.   D.S.

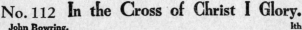

In the cross, in the cross, Be my glo - ry ev - er;

No. 112   In the Cross of Christ I Glory.

John Bowring.   Ithamar Conkey.

M. 100

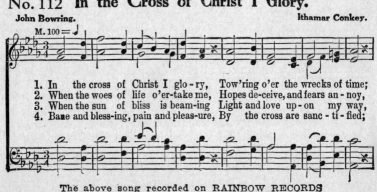

1. In the cross of Christ I glo - ry, Tow'ring o'er the wrecks of time;
2. When the woes of life o'er-take me, Hopes de-ceive, and fears an - noy,
3. When the sun of bliss is beam-ing Light and love up - on my way,
4. Bane and bless-ing, pain and pleas-ure, By the cross are sanc - ti - fied;

The above song recorded on RAINBOW RECORDS

In the Cross of Christ I Glory.

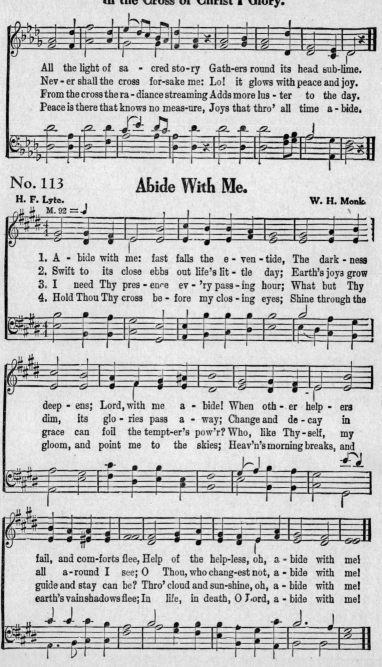

All the light of sa - cred sto-ry Gath-ers round its head sub-lime.
Nev - er shall the cross for-sake me: Lo! it glows with peace and joy.
From the cross the ra - diance streaming Adds more lus - ter to the day.
Peace is there that knows no meas-ure, Joys that thro' all time a - bide.

No. 113

Abide With Me.

H. F. Lyte.

W. H. Monk.

M. 92 = ♩

1. A - bide with me: fast falls the e - ven-tide, The dark-ness
2. Swift to its close ebbs out life's lit - tle day; Earth's joys grow
3. I need Thy pres-ence ev - 'ry pass-ing hour; What but Thy
4. Hold Thou Thy cross be - fore my clos-ing eyes; Shine through the

deep - ens; Lord, with me a - bide! When oth - er help - ers
dim, its glo - ries pass a - way; Change and de - cay in
grace can foil the tempt-er's pow'r? Who, like Thy - self, my
gloom, and point me to the skies; Heav'n's morning breaks, and

fail, and com-forts flee, Help of the help-less, oh, a - bide with me!
all a - round I see; O Thou, who chang-est not, a - bide with me!
guide and stay can be? Thro' cloud and sun-shine, oh, a - bide with me!
earth's vain shadows flee; In life, in death, O Lord, a - bide with me!

No. 114   EVEN ME.

Mrs. Elizabeth Codner.   Wm. B. Bradbury.

1. {Lord, I hear of show'rs of bless-ing Thou art scat-t'ring full and free;
Show'rs, the thirst-y land re-fresh-ing; Let some drop-pings fall on me.}
2. {Pass me not, O gra-cious Fa-ther, Sin-ful though my heart may be;
Thou mightst leave me, but the rath-er Let Thy mer-cy fall on me.}
3. {Pass me not, O ten-der Sav-ior, Let me love and cling to Thee;
I am long-ing for Thy fa-vor; Whilst Thou'rt calling, O call me.}

E-ven me, E-ven me, Let Thy bless-ing fall on me.

No. 115   REVIVE US AGAIN.

Wm. P. Mackay.   J. J. Husband.

1. We praise Thee, O God, for the Son of Thy love, For Jesus, who died, and is now gone above.
2. All glory and praise to the Lamb that was slain, Who has borne all our sins and has cleansed ev'ry stain.
3. All glory and praise to the God of all grace, Who has bought us, and sought us, and guided our ways.
4. Revive us again; fill each heart with Thy love; May each soul be rekindled with fire from above.

Chorus

Hal-le-lu-jah! Thine the glo-ry, Hal-le-lu-jah! A-men, Re-vive us a-gain.

No. 116   HAPPY DAY.

Philip Doddridge.   E. F. Rimbault.

1. {O hap-py day, that fixed my choice On Thee, my Sav-ior and my God!
Well may this glowing heart rejoice, And tell its rap-tures all a-broad.} Hap-py

Fine.   D. S.

day, happy day, When Jesus wash'd my sins away! {He taught me how to watch and pray,
And live re-joic-ing ev-'ry day.}

2 O happy bond, that seals my vows
To Him who merits all my love!
Let cheerful anthems fill His house,
While to that sacred shrine I move.

3 'Tis done; the great transaction's done!
I am my Lord's and He is mine;
He drew me, and I followed on,
Charmed to confess the voice divine.

Missionary Songs

117 **Ready**

COPYRIGHT, 1903, BY CHARLIE D. TILLMAN

S. E. L.   Charlie D. Tillman

1. Read-y to suf-fer grief or pain, Read-y to stand the test;
2. Read-y to go, read-y to bear, Read-y to watch and pray;
3. Read-y to speak, read-y to think, Read-y with heart and brain;
4. Read-y to speak, read-y to warn, Read-y o'er souls to yearn;

Read-y to stay at home and send Oth-ers, if He sees best.
Read-y to stand a-side and give, Till He shall clear the way.
Read-y to stand where He sees fit, Read-y to stand the strain.
Read-y in life, or read-y in death, Read-y for His re-turn.

CHORUS

Read-y to go, read-y to stay, Read-y my place to fill;

Read-y for serv-ice, low-ly or great, Read-y to do His will.

Jesus Saves!

Priscilla J. Owens. COPYRIGHT OF JOHN J. HOOD. USED BY PER. Wm. J. Kirkpatrick.

1. We have heard the joy-ful sound: Je-sus saves! Je-sus saves!
2. Waft it on the roll-ing tide: Je-sus saves! Je-sus saves!
3. Sing a-bove the bat-tle strife, Je-sus saves! Je-sus saves!
4. Give the winds a might-y voice: Je-sus saves! Je-sus saves!

Spread the ti-dings all a-round: Je-sus saves! Je-sus saves!
Tell to sin-ners far and wide: Je-sus saves! Je-sus saves!
By His death and end-less life, Je-sus saves! Je-sus saves!
Let the na-tions now re-joice,— Je-sus saves! Je-sus saves!

Bear the news to ev-'ry land, Climb the steeps and cross the waves;
Sing, ye is-lands of the sea, Ech-o back, ye o-cean caves;
Sing it soft-ly thro' the gloom, When the heart for mer-cy craves;
Shout sal-va-tion full and free, High-est hills and deep-est caves;

On-ward! —'tis our Lord's com-mand; Je-sus saves! Je-sus saves!
Earth shall keep her ju-bi-lee: Je-sus saves! Je-sus saves!
Sing in tri-umph o'er the tomb,— Je-sus saves! Je-sus saves!
This our song of vic-to-ry,— Je-sus saves! Je-sus saves!

No. 119   SEND THE LIGHT.

C. H. G.

CHAS. H. GABRIEL.

1. There's a call comes ringing o'er the rest-less wave, "Send the light!
2. We have heard the Ma-ce-do-nian call to-day,
3. Let us pray that grace may ev-'ry-where a-bound,
4. Let us not grow wear-y in the work of love, "Send the light!

Send the light!" There are souls to res-cue, there are souls to save,
And a gold-en of-f'ring at the cross we lay,
And a Christ-like spir-it ev-'ry-where be found,
Send the light!" Let us gath-er jew-els for a crown a-bove,

Send the light!...... Send the light!............
Send the light! Send the light!

CHORUS.

Send the light, ... the bless-ed gos- pel light, Let it
Send the light, ... and let its ra- diant beams Light the

shine....... from shore to shore!...........
world....... for-ev-er- [Omit. . . .] more. (for-ev-er-more.)

Bringing In the Sheaves.

Knowles Shaw.   George A. Minor.

M. 92 = ♩

1. Sow-ing in the morning, sow-ing seeds of kind-ness, Sow-ing in the
2. Sow-ing in the sunshine, sow-ing in the shad-ows, Fear-ing nei-ther
3. Go then, ev-er weep-ing, sow-ing for the Mas-ter, Tho' the loss sus-

noon-tide and the dew-y eve; Wait-ing for the har-vest and the
clouds nor win-ter's chill-ing breeze; By and by the har-vest and the
tained, our spir-it oft-en grieves; When our weeping's o-ver, He will

time of reap-ing, We shall come re-joic-ing, bringing in the sheaves.
la-bor end-ed, We shall come re-joic-ing, bringing in the sheaves.
bid us wel-come, We shall come re-joic-ing, bringing in the sheaves.

CHORUS.

Bring-ing in the sheaves, bringing in the sheaves, We shall come re-joic-ing,

bringing in the sheaves. We shall come re-joic-ing, bringing in the sheaves.

Rescue the Perishing.

FANNY J. CROSBY.

W. H. DOANE.

1. Res - cue the per - ish - ing, Care for the dy - ing, Snatch them in
2. Tho' they are slight-ing him, Still he is wait - ing, Wait - ing the
3. Down in the hu - man heart, Crushed by the tempt - er, Feel - ings lie
4. Res - cue the per - ish - ing, Du - ty de - mands it; Strength for thy

pit - y from sin and the grave; Weep o'er the err-ing one, Lift up the
pen - i - tent child to re - ceive. Plead with them earn-est-ly, Plead with them
bur-ied that grace can re - store: Touched by a lov - ing heart Wakened by
la - bor the Lord will pro-vide; Back to the nar - row way Pa - tient-ly

CHORUS.

fall - en, Tell them of Je - sus, the might - y to save.
gen - tly: He will for - give if they on - ly be - lieve. Res - cue the
kindness, Chords that were bro - ken will vi - brate once more.
win them; Tell the poor wand'rer a Sav - ior has died.

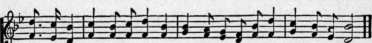

per - ish-ing, Care for the dy - ing; Je - sus is mer-ci - ful, Je - sus will save.

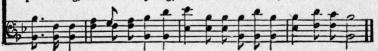

No. 122. TO THE WORK.

Fanny J. Crosby.

W. H. Doane.

1. To the work! to the work! we are ser-vants of God, Let us fol-low the path that our Mas-ter has trod; With the balm of His counsel our strength to re-new,

2. To the work! to the work! let the hun-gry be fed, To the foun-tain of life let the wea-ry be led; In the cross and the ban-ner our glo-ry shall be,

3. To the work! to the work! there is la-bor for all, For the kingdom of dark-ness and er-ror shall fall; And the name of Je-ho-vah ex-alt-ed shall be,

4. To the work! to the work! in the strength of the Lord, And a robe and a crown shall our la-bor re-ward; When the home of the faith-ful our dwelling shall be,

CHORUS.

Let us do with our might what our hands find to do, Toil-ing on,

While we her-ald the tid-ings, *"Sal-va-tion is free."*

In the loud swell-ing chorus, *"Sal-va-tion is free."*

And we shout with the ransomed, *"Sal-va-tion is free."*

Toil-ing on toil-ing on, (toil-ing on,) Toil-ing on, (toil-ing on,) toil-ing on, (toil-ing on,)

Let us hope (and trust) Let us watch (and pray,) And la-bor till the Mas-ter comes.

Copyright 1899, by W. H. Doane.

No. 123 Throw Out The Life-Line.

E. S. Ufford.

E. S. Ufford. Arr. by Geo. C. Stebbins.

1. Throw out the Life-Line a-cross the dark wave, There is a broth-er whom
2. Throw out the Life-Line with hand quick and strong; Why do you tar-ry, why
3. Throw out the Life-Line to dan-ger-fraught men, Sink-ing in an-guish where
4. Soon will the sea-son of res-cue be o'er, Soon will they drift to e-

some one should save; Some-bod-y's broth-er! oh, who then, will dare To
lin-ger so long? See! he is sink-ing; oh, has-ten to-day—And
you've nev-er been; Winds of temp-ta-tion and bil-lows of woe Will
ter-ni-ty's shore, Haste then, my broth-er, no time for de-lay, But

CHORUS.

throw out the Life-Line, his per-il to share?
out with the Life-Boat! a-way, then, a-way! Throw out the Life-Line!
soon hurl them out where the dark wa-ters flow.
throw out the Life-Line and save them to-day.

Throw out the Life-Line! Some-one is drift-ing a-way; Throw out the

Life-Line! Throw out the Life-Line! Some-one is sink-ing to-day.

Shall We Meet?

HORACE L. HASTINGS.　　　　　　　　ELIHU S. RICE.

1　Shall we meet be-yond the riv-er, Where the surges cease to roll?
2.　Shall we meet in that blest harbor, When our stormy voy-age's o'er
3.　Shall we meet in yon-der cit-y, Where the tow'rs of crys-tal shine?
4.　Shall we meet with Christ, our Savior, When he comes to claim his own?

Where, in all the bright for-ev-er, Sorrow ne'er shall press the soul?
Shall we meet and cast the an-chor By the fair, ce-les-tial shore?
Where the walls are all of jas-per, Built by work-man-ship di-vine?
Shall we know his blessed fa-vor, And sit down up-on his throne?

CHORUS.

Shall we meet, shall we meet, Shall we meet beyond the riv-er?

Shall we meet be-yond the riv-er, Where the sur-ges cease to roll?

By permission.

Invitation Hymns

No. 125   I Hear Thy Welcome Voice.

L. H.   Rev. L. Hartsough.

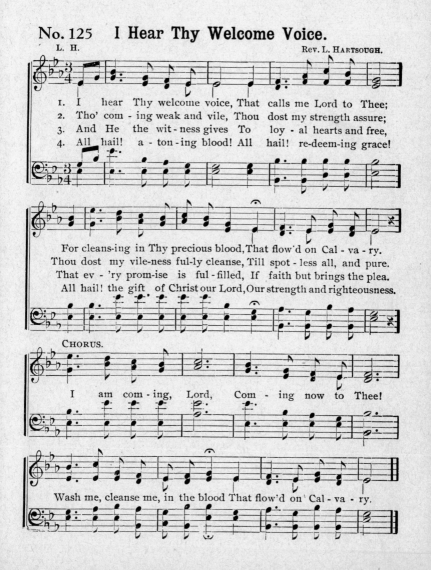

1. I hear Thy welcome voice, That calls me Lord to Thee;
2. Tho' com - ing weak and vile, Thou dost my strength assure;
3. And He the wit - ness gives To loy - al hearts and free,
4. All hail! a - ton - ing blood! All hail! re - deem - ing grace!

For cleans-ing in Thy precious blood, That flow'd on Cal - va - ry.
Thou dost my vile-ness ful-ly cleanse, Till spot - less all, and pure.
That ev - 'ry prom-ise is ful - filled, If faith but brings the plea.
All hail! the gift of Christ our Lord, Our strength and righteousness.

Chorus.

I am com - ing, Lord, Com - ing now to Thee!

Wash me, cleanse me, in the blood That flow'd on Cal - va - ry.

Softly and Tenderly.

W. L. T.

Will L. Thompson.

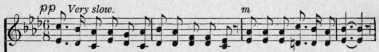

1. Soft-ly and ten-der-ly Je-sus is call-ing, Call-ing for you and for me;
2. Why should we tarry when Jesus is pleading, Pleading for you and for me?
3. Time is now fleeting, the moments are passing, Passing from you and from me;
4. Oh! for the won-der-ful love He has promised, Promised for you and for me;

See   on the portals He's waiting and watching, Watching for you and for me.
Why should we linger and heed not His mer-cies, Mer-cies for you and for me?
Shadows are gathering, death beds are com-ing, Com-ing for you and for me.
Tho' we have sinned, He has mercy and par-don, Par-don for you and for me.

CHORUS.

Come home,.. come home,.... Ye who are wear-y, come home;..
Come home,   come home,

Ear-nest-ly, ten-der-ly, Je-sus is call-ing, Call-ing, O sin-ner, come home!

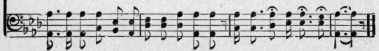

127 Jesus is Calling.

Fanny J. Crosby.   George C. Stebbins.

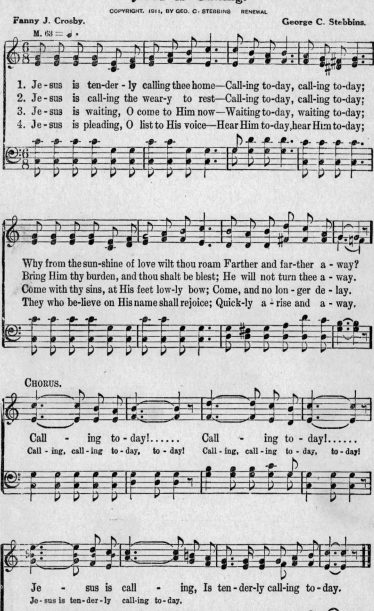

1. Je-sus is ten-der-ly calling thee home—Call-ing to-day, call-ing to-day;
2. Je-sus is call-ing the wear-y to rest—Call-ing to-day, call-ing to-day;
3. Je-sus is waiting, O come to Him now—Waiting to-day, waiting to-day;
4. Je-sus is pleading, O list to His voice—Hear Him to-day, hear Him to-day;

Why from the sun-shine of love wilt thou roam Farther and far-ther a-way?
Bring Him thy burden, and thou shalt be blest; He will not turn thee a-way.
Come with thy sins, at His feet low-ly bow; Come, and no lon-ger de-lay.
They who be-lieve on His name shall rejoice; Quick-ly a-rise and a-way.

CHORUS.

Call - ing to-day!...... Call - ing to-day!......
Call-ing, call-ing to-day, to-day! Call-ing, call-ing to-day, to-day!

Je - sus is call - ing, Is ten-der-ly call-ing to-day.
Je-sus is ten-der-ly call-ing to-day.

128 Just As I Am.

Charlotte Elliott.

Wm. B. Bradbury.

M. 100 = ♩

1. Just as I am, with-out one plea, But that Thy blood was shed for me,
2. Just as I am, and wait-ing not To rid my soul of one dark blot,
3. Just as I am, tho' tossed a-bout With man-y a con-flict, man-y a doubt,
4. Just as I am, poor, wretched, blind, Sight, rich-es, heal-ing of the mind,
5. Just as I am, Thou wilt re-ceive, Wilt welcome, par-don, cleanse, relieve;
6. Just as I am, Thy love un-known Hath bro-ken ev-'ry bar-rier down;

And that Thou bidd'st me come to Thee, O Lamb of God, I come! I come!
To Thee, whose blood can cleanse each spot, O Lamb of God, I come! I come!
Fight-ings with-in, and fears with-out, O Lamb of God, I come! I come!
Yea, all I need, in Thee to find, O Lamb of God, I come! I come!
Be-cause Thy prom-ise I be-lieve, O Lamb of God, I come! I come!
Now, to be Thine, yea, Thine a-lone, O Lamb of God, I come! I come!

129 Oh, Why Not To-night?

USED BY PERMISSION.

J. Calvin Bushey.

M. 96 = ♩

1. Oh, do not let the word de-part, And close thine eyes a-gainst the light;
2. To-mor-row's sun may nev-er rise To bless thy long de-lud-ed sight;
3. Our Lord in pit-y lin-gers still, And wilt thou thus His love re-quite?
4. Our bless-ed Lord re-fus-es none Who would to Him their souls u-nite;

Poor sin-ner, hard-en not your heart, Be saved, oh, to-night.
This is the time, oh, then, be wise, Be saved, oh, to-night.
Re-nounce at once thy stub-born will, Be saved, oh, to-night.
Be-lieve, o-bey, the work is done, Be saved, oh, to-night.

Oh, Why Not To-night?

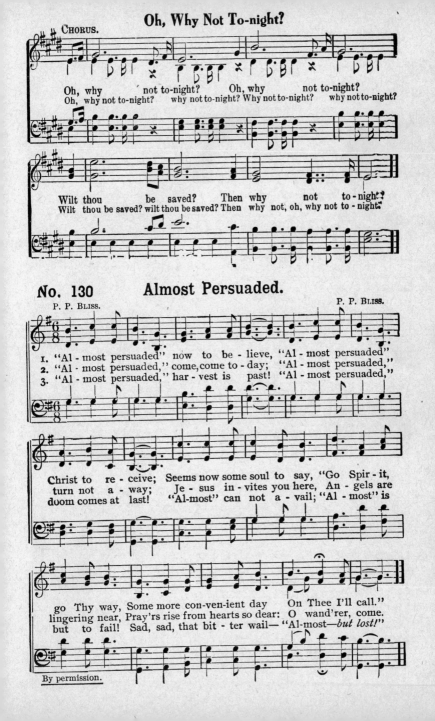

CHORUS.

Oh, why not to-night? Oh, why not to-night?
Oh, why not to-night? why not to-night? Why not to-night? why not to-night?

Wilt thou be saved? Then why not to-night?
Wilt thou be saved? wilt thou be saved? Then why not, oh, why not to-night?

No. 130   Almost Persuaded.

P. P. BLISS.   P. P. BLISS.

1. "Al - most persuaded" now to be - lieve, "Al - most persuaded"
2. "Al - most persuaded," come, come to - day; "Al - most persuaded,"
3. "Al - most persuaded," har - vest is past! "Al - most persuaded,"

Christ to re - ceive; Seems now some soul to say, "Go Spir - it,
turn not a - way; Je - sus in - vites you here, An - gels are
doom comes at last! "Al-most" can not a - vail; "Al - most" is

go Thy way, Some more con-ven-ient day On Thee I'll call."
lingering near, Pray'rs rise from hearts so dear: O wand'rer, come.
but to fail! Sad, sad, that bit - ter wail— "Al-most—*but lost!*"

By permission.

His Way With Thee.

Psalm 37: 5.
(CONSECRATION.)

C. S. N.

COPYRIGHT. 1909, BY H. L. GILMOUR.

Rev. Cyrus S. Nusbaum.

1. Would you live for Je-sus, and be always pure and good? Would you walk with
Him with-in the nar-row road? Would you have Him bear your bur-den,
car-ry all your load? Let Him have His way with thee.

2. Would you have Him make you free, and fol-low at His call? Would you know the
peace that comes by giv-ing all? Would you have Him save you, so that
you need never fall? Let Him have His way with thee.

3. Would you in His kingdom find a place of constant rest? Would you prove Him
true each prov-i-den-tial test? Would you in His serv-ice la-bor
always at your best? Let Him have His way with thee.

CHORUS.

His pow'r can make you what you ought to be; His blood can cleanse your heart and make you free; His love can fill your soul, and you will see 'Twas best for Him to have His way with thee.

rit.

No. 132 — There's a Great Day Coming.

W. L. T.   WILL L. THOMPSON.

1. There's a great day coming, A great day coming, There's a great day com-ing by and by;
2. There's a bright day coming, A bright day coming, There's a bright day com-ing by and by;
3. There's a sad day coming, A sad day coming, There's a sad day com-ing by and by;

When the saints and the sinners shall be parted right and left,
But its brightness shall only come to them that love the Lord, Are you ready for that day to come,
When the sinner shall hear his doom, "Depart, I know ye not,"

CHORUS. m pp

Are you ready? Are you ready? Are you ready for the judgment day? For the judgment day?

No. 133 — Pass Me Not.

FANNY J. CROSBY.   Copyright renewed 1899, by W. H. Doane.   W. H. DOANE.

1. Pass me not, O gen-tle Sav-ior, Hear my hum-ble cry; While on
2. Let me at the throne of mer-cy Find a sweet re-lief; Kneel-ing
3. Trust-ing on-ly in Thy mer-it, Would I seek Thy face; Heal my
4. Thou the Spring of all my com-fort, More than life to me, Whom have

CHORUS.

oth-ers thou art smil-ing, Do not pass me by.
there in deep con-tri-tion, Help my un-be-lief. Sav-ior, Sav-ior,
wounded, brok-en spir-it, Save me by Thy grace.
I on earth be-side Thee? Whom in heav'n but Thee?

Hear my hum-ble cry, While on oth-ers Thou art call-ing, Do not pass me by.

Children's Songs

No. 134   **Victory**

Evangeline Price   Copyright, 1941, by Don. F. Price   Evangeline Price

Saved, saved, saved, I'm liv - ing for Je - sus each day;

Joy, joy, joy, my soul is re-joicing since He came to stay. Love, love,

love, so rich and so bound-less and free, He cleans-es from

sin, giving sweet peace within; I have vic - to - ry.

No. 135   Go To Sunday School

E. B.   Copyright, 1941, by The Boone Publishing Co.   Edward Boone

1. Here's a heart-y wel-come to our Sun-day School, Our Sun-day School, Our
2. Ev-'ry-bod-y ought to go to Sun-day School, To Sun-day School, To
3. Ev-'ry-bod-y ought to stay for preach-ing too, For preach-ing too, For

Sun-day School; We are glad that you are here, Come each Sun-day
Sun-day School; We should learn our les-son well, Be there when they
preach-ing too; If you are not in your place, They will miss your

of the year. Here's a heart-y wel-come to our Sun-day School.
ring the bell. Ev-'ry-bod-y ought to go to Sun-day School.
smil-ing face. Ev-'ry-bod-y ought to stay for preach-ing too.

No. 136   Living For Jesus

Copyright, 1938, by the Boone Publishing Co.

Har. by Mrs. Edward Boone   Edward Boone

Liv-ing for Je-sus, liv-ing each day, Hap-py in ser-vice, glad to o-bey,

Rit.

Tell-ing the sto-ry of the nar-row way, I'm liv-ing for Christ, my King.

137 How Do You Feel?

Clayton P. Shepherd

Anonymous

1. How do you feel, Broth-er Chris-tian, How do you feel?
2. How do you feel, Broth-er Chris-tian, How do you feel?
3. How do you feel, Broth-er Chris-tian, How do you feel?
4. How do you feel, Broth-er Chris-tian, How do you feel?
5. How do you feel, Broth-er Chris-tian, How do you feel?
6. How do you feel, Broth-er Chris-tian, How do you feel?

That we're hap-py you are here we can't con-ceal:
Is the Gos-pel of our Lord a-live and real?
Are you hid-ing some-thing you would not re-veal?
Do you thank our God in heav-en for each meal?
As you read your Sun-day pa-per, do you kneel?
When you gai-ly watch the whirl-ing mov-ie reel,

We are here to sing and pray, Preach and praise, and, by the
Are you liv-ing, full and free; Is your soul at lib-er-
When you use the Ho-ly Day Just to ride a-round and
Do you thank Him, as you're fed, For your meat and dai-ly
Do you pray and thank the press For your world-ly care-less-
When you sit on Sun-day night, In its ar-ti-fi-cial

way, How do you feel, Broth-er Chris-tian, How do you feel?
ty? How do you feel, Broth-er Chris-tian, How do you feel?
play, How do you feel, Broth-er Chris-tian, How do you feel?
bread? How do you feel, Broth-er Chris-tian, How do you feel?
ness? How do you feel, Broth-er Chris-tian, How do you feel?
light, How do you feel, Broth-er Chris-tian, How do you feel?

138 This Little Light of Mine

Arrangement by Edward Boone

Anonymous

1. This lit-tle light of mine, I'm gon-na let it shine;
2. When I'm in the val-ley, I'm gon-na let it shine;
3. In my neigh-bor's house, I'm gon-na let it shine;
4. When I meet with hard-ships, I'm gon-na let it shine;

This lit-tle light of mine, I'm gon-na let it shine;
When I'm in the val-ley, I'm gon-na let it shine;
In my neigh-bor's house, I'm gon-na let it shine;
When I meet with hard-ships, I'm gon-na let it shine;

This lit-tle light of mine, I'm gon-na let it shine;
When I'm in the val-ley, I'm gon-na let it shine;
In my neigh-bor's house, I'm gon-na let it shine;
When I meet with hard-ships, I'm gon-na let it shine;

Let it shine, let it shine, let it shine (let it shine).
Let it shine, let it shine, let it shine (let it shine).
Let it shine, let it shine, let it shine (let it shine).
Let it shine, let it shine, let it shine (let it shine).

139 I'll Be List'ning

New arrangement by Edward Boone

Anonymous

1. When He calls me, I will an - - swer; When He
    1. When He calls me, I will an - swer, I will an - swer;
2. When He calls me, I'll be ris - - ing; When He
    2. When He calls me, I'll be ris - ing, I'll be ris - ing;
3 When He calls me, I'll be like Him; When He
    3. When He calls me, I'll be like Him, I'll be like Him;
4. When He calls me, I'll be read - - y; When He
    4. When He calls me, I'll be read - y, I'll be read - y;

calls me, I will an - - swer; When He calls me,
  When He calls me, I will an - swer, I will an - swer;   When He calls me,
calls me, I'll be ris - - ing; When He calls me,
  When He calls me, I'll be ris - ing, I'll be ris - ing;   When He calls me,
calls me, I'll be like - - Him; When He calls me,
  When He calls me, I'll be like Him, I'll be like Him;   When He calls me,
calls me, I'll be read - - y; When He calls me,
  When He calls me, I'll be read - y, I'll be read - y;   When He calls me,

I will an - swer; I'll be somewhere, list'ning for my name. . . . . .
I'll be ris - ing; I'll be somewhere, list'ning for my name. . . . . .
I'll be like Him; I'll be somewhere, list'ning for my name. . . . . .
I'll be read - y; I'll be somewhere, list'ning for my name. . . . . .
    I'll be list'ning for my name.

CHORUS

Oh, I'll be somewhere, list'ning; I'll be somewhere, list'ning; I'll be somewhere,

I'll Be List'ning

list'ning for my name. . . . . . Oh, I'll be somewhere, list'ning; I'll be
list'ning for my name.

somewhere, list'ning; I'll be somewhere, list'ning for my name. . . . . .
I'll be list'ning for my name.

140   I Love Jesus

Arrangement by Edward Boone   Anonymous

1. Oh, I love Je-sus (So do I); Oh, I love Je-sus (So do I);
2. I'm goin' to heav-en (So am I); I'm goin' to heav-en (So am I);
3. I hate the dev-il (So do I); I hate the dev-il (So do I);
4. Oh, hal-le-lu-jah (Praise the Lord)! Oh, hal-le-lu-jah (Praise the Lord)!
5. I'm feel-ing bet-ter (So am I); I'm feel-ing bet-ter (So am I);

Oh, I love Je-sus (So do I); Oh, I love Je-sus (So do I).
I'm goin' to heav-en (So am I); I'm goin' to heav-en (So am I).
I hate the dev-il (So do I); I hate the dev-il (So do I).
Oh, hal-le-lu-jah (Praise the Lord)! Oh, hal-le-lu-jah (Praise the Lord)!
I'm feel-ing bet-ter (So am I); I'm feel-ing bet-ter (So am I).

1-5. Oh, I love Je-sus; He's my Sav-iour; He smiles and He loves me too.

No. 141   We'll Outshine the Sun

New arrangement by Edward Boone

1. If Je-sus is our Savior, We will out-shine the sun; We will out-shine
2. If we keep blest and hap-py, We will out-shine the sun; We will out-shine
3. Keep on the Gos-pel high-way And you'll out-shine the sun; You will out-shine
4. Don't talk about your neighbor, And you'll out-shine the sun; You will out-shine

the sun; Yes, we'll out-shine the sun. If we keep true to Je-sus, We will
the sun; Yes, we'll out-shine the sun. If we keep shun-ning e - vil, We will
the sun; Yes, you'll out-shine the sun. Just fol-low all the signboards, And you'll
the sun; Yes, you'll out-shine the sun. Don't talk a-bout your preacher, And you'll

Chorus

out-shine the sun, And we'll walk the gold-en streets on high.
out-shine the sun, And we'll walk the gold-en streets on high. Bye and bye we'll
out-shine the sun, And you'll walk the gold-en streets on high.
out-shine the sun, And you'll walk the gold-en streets on high.

sure - ly see the King; Bye and bye we'll sure - ly see the King,

Bye and bye we'll sure-ly see the King, And we'll walk the golden streets on high.

No. 142

Jesus Is Near

Evangeline Price
Copyright, 1941, by Don F. Price
Evangeline Price

Je-sus is near; Je-sus is near; He hears me when I pray.

Je-sus is near; He gives me cheer; He loves me ev-'ry day.

No. 143

Happy Children

Evangeline Price
Copyright, 1941, by Don F. Price
Evangeline Price

We are hap-py chil-dren, yes, we are; Smil-ing hap-py children,

yes, we are. Je-sus saves from ev-'ry sin, mak-ing us so pure with-

in; We are hap-py chil-dren, yes, we are.

Index